incognito

A COLLECTION BY DAVID YOUNG

WITH PHOTOGRAPHS BY JIM LANG

THE COACH HOUSE PRESS, TORONTO

By the same author
Agent Provocateur

Early drafts of some of these stories appeared in
Bombay Gin, Impulse, NMFG, Only Paper, Periodics and *Writing*.

The Robert Smithson quote reprinted by permission from
'Incidents of Mirror Travel in the Yucatan,' *Artforum,* September, 1969.

Cover collage by the author

Special thanks to Nelson Adams, Stan Bevington, Dennis Lee,
David McFadden and Michael Ondaatje for the help and
encouragement they provided during the editing of this book.

Published with the assistance of the Canada Council
and the Ontario Arts Council.

ISBN 0-88910-204-X

This collection grew out of my curiosity about the border-blur between autobiography and fiction. I wanted to cross over into that zone and examine the way we use it to remake ourselves and believe in the world. It's worth noting that all the characters were closely shadowed by real people when they entered this book. I've tried to tell their stories with the same honesty I'd expect of you if we met in the cocktail lounge of a snowed-in airport.

I'm deeply indebted to Jim Lang whose remarkable archive of self-portraits sparked my initial intuitions and structured their development. Without Lang's photographs nothing would have been possible.

The book as a whole is dedicated to Sarah, who continues to make me a different person, and to the fond memory of David Phipps, my godfather, who taught me how to make angels in the snow.

DY / Toronto / May '82

Thirty years is as much to understand
As a nickel's worth of movie
    a cloth moist with
Miles of wild strawberries
A decade of moon hours
Events in a line
Traced by squeezing shaping
        shaking fingers
Toward a pointless sacred habit of memory
Not as a document of a way
But a scratch on the glass eye of hindsight.

JIM LANG

Remembrances are but numbers on a map, vacant memories constellating the intangible terrains in deleted vicinities. It is the dimension of absence which remains to be found. The expunged colour which remains to be seen. The fictive voices of the totems have exhausted their arguments. Yucatan is elsewhere.

ROBERT SMITHSON

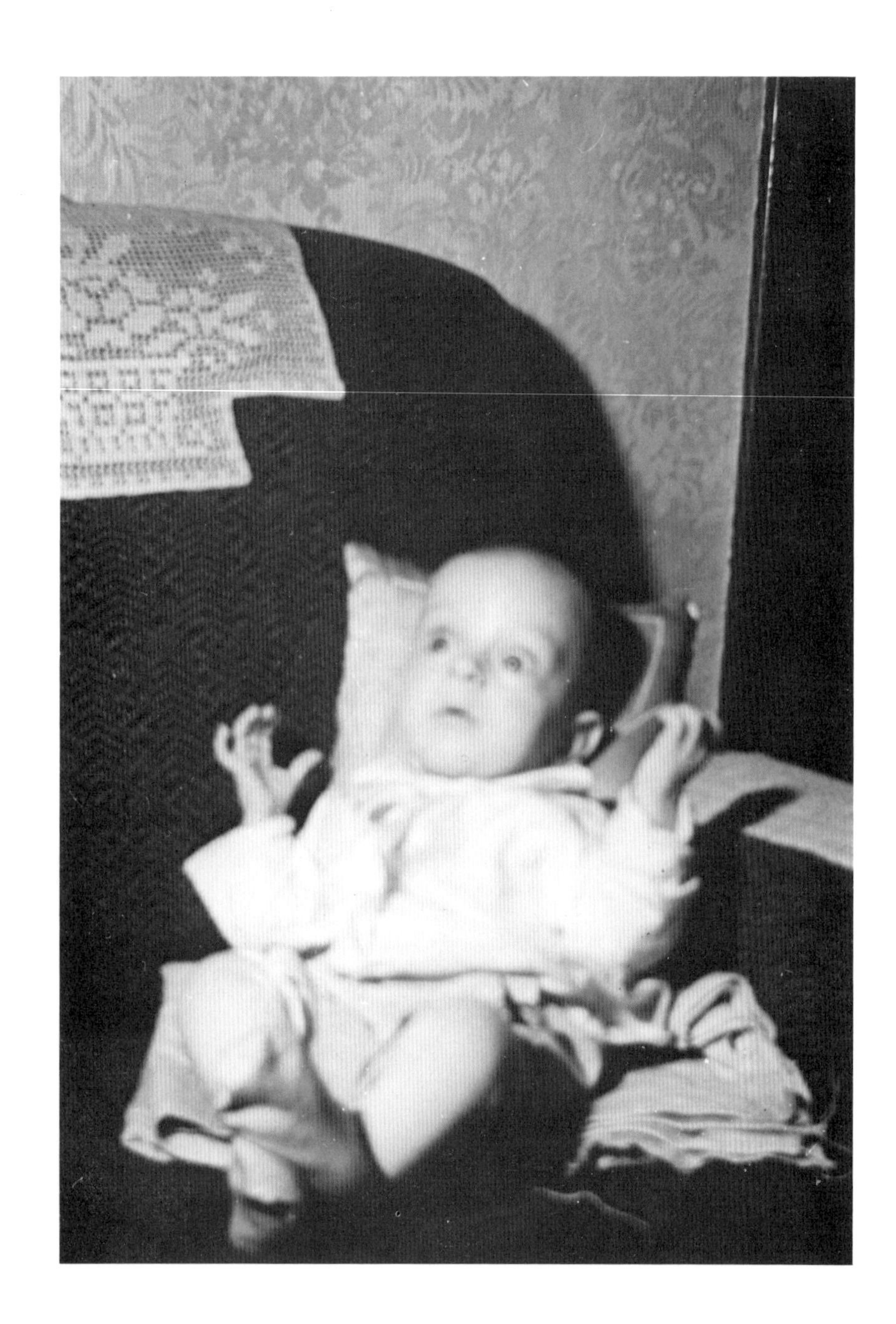

Tabula Rasa

Joseph Stalin

I don't think I had a childhood as that state is customarily understood. Browsing through any stranger's family album I invariably locate a face which could only have belonged to me. I'm no fool and I know a head-game when I see one. This particular doppelganger is a direct throwback to a tribal ritual we performed every Spring when the Equinox sunrise came through that slit in the sacred rock – everyone in my family marching around caked in white mud looking for all the world like so many dazed survivors from a radio-triggered explosion in a Sicilian bakery. But that's another story...

The point is, all my early memories depend entirely on the lavishly embroidered testimony of other witnesses – those much-loved tribal elders who stage-managed my memories to conform to folklores they themselves inherited in childhoods yet more distant. Since the elders controlled the rear-view mirror, and were forever tinkering with the scenes it reflected, the child I remember is a collage of faces, all of which share that arching eyebrow which characterized the state of mind where my people lived.

Sometimes I feel like that grandson of Joseph Stalin who spends his days in a Lubinsk mirror factory watching details vanish from a half-erased drawing he calls his face.

Edith Sitwell

How am I to deal with the limitlessly variable footage that can be synched up with this inherited hindsight? I could quite handily

prove my parents' claim that they were both preoccupied with their impoverished circumstances as grad students and got caught flat-footed by the arrival of identical twins – shocked into pagan chants when the stronger of the two died inexplicably a week later. Or perhaps my father, enjoying his hair shirt the way a psoriasis sufferer enjoys a loofah, chose to convince me that he was reincarnated as an alcoholic butcher on the day of my birth. Shouting threats at my mother in the kitchen, throwing his bloody apron in her face as the screen door slammed on another of those pitch black nights he used to escape. My mother weeping quietly by the fridge, little me quaking on her hip, a terrified two-year-old lover. Or maybe, on the spur of a moment, they decided to splice in some exotic locations. Used a handful of corroborating postcards to convince me that I came into this world on the third floor of a Left Bank rooming house. How about a cameo role for one of those Edith Sitwell-type character actresses? Write in some pick-up dialogue for a wise old grandmother who lived in an apartment over the garage and taught me how to stammer in Gaelic before I could stammer in English?

Still with me, Mel? You're gonna love this one! We trot out the old chestnut about the Christmas tree in August! Stick the little bugger with one of those rare blood diseases! Have him learning how to swim with bread bags wrapped around a leg cast! ... Mel? Hey, c'mon back fella! It's not carved in stone for crissakes! We can push this baby anyplace we like!

The First Law of Television

Anything that is repeated often enough eventually turns into a fact carrying the same weight as 'the sky is blue.' This is the mind-splice inside those simu-walnut cabinets manufactured for us by the very jolly and physically fit workers of Japan. This is the virus responsible for the curvature of imagination.

A Good Shot at the Samsonite Luggage

The likeliest possibility of all is that the occasions of my upbringing were so commonplace and widely shared that their actual substance evaporated from lack of attention – that saucer of dried milk one finds in the narrow space between the fridge and the wall many months after the lovably overweight cat, pink gut protruding, has been carted off to the vet for a 100 cc's of cosmic bliss.

One way or another I desperately want to establish myself as a singularly identifiable entity who was at large in the past. Oddly, this seems the only sure way to guarantee my safe passage through the indefinites of a present that looks me square in the eye like a high school gym teacher and says:

'Hey guy, some kinda *desire* you showed us out there! Bet your sneakers if times were any easier you'd be walking away from those compulsories with a handful of fives and sixes – maybe even a few sevens if we had an Aussie on the judges' stand. Obviously no way we can advance you to the Regionals – but you've got nothing to hang your head about! You still got one helluva shot at the Samsonite luggage, not to mention that deluxe dinner for two at Sai Woo. Cheer up! You'll hear from our people one way or the other ... oh, before I forget ... could you hustle up to the tote room and hand in those snapshots? Our management guys are caught in a bit of an inventory squeeze – we got trainees camped out in sleeping bags all the way around the building and down the next block!'

The Past

My hesitation would vanish in a moment if I could take down these snapshots and use the empty wall to project some of the footage I really believe in. Here's the scenario: this cabin fades slowly to black. Silence punctuated by the odd cough, the guilty crinkle of a hand foraging for Licorice Allsorts, another throat clears, then –

BARTOK!

– the low keening of a solitary cello, the bow lifting mid-phrase so there'll be silence when the first sprockets rattle into the gate to split the darkness with that unbending blue beam that turns cigarette smoke into art.

The past I want you to see is a time-lapse documentary. A loop of stop-action footage that recycles itself every sixty seconds. The single frames were exposed by a custom-mounted Airflex that's been trained on the scene outside this cabin window since the moment of my birth, its shutter triggered twice a month as year inched into year.

On the left-hand margin of the frame you'll see that stand of hardwoods I'm looking at right now. In the mid-ground a single gnarled jackpine trailing its teardrop gesture along the wind. Foreground flowing to background down this same changeless slope of pink granite. Along the upper margin, the empty horizon and that lonely whaleback reef surfacing for air. In the course of this sixty-second loop we'll see entire years foreshorten into blips that spike-spike-spike, and disappear. Summers shimmering in skyburst – a momentary radiance of incandescent chlorophyll that sucks itself back with a crackling sigh. All the events between me and the summer of 1946 collapsed into that background blur of pure Nature which separates me from everything I need to remember.

The Future

When I visualize the future, I project onto the empty space behind the bathroom mirror – the place where no one looks until that Saturday morning when it's time to repaint. The routines of some anonymous weekend magically transformed as the mirror comes down off the wall – the rectangle of 'original colour' a frame for the future, its boundaries demarcated by grubby fingerprints from countless morning examinations, toothpaste spatters from a thousand late and mournful nights.

'This is the way it originally was,' we remind ourselves, the bathroom mirror leaned against the wall at our feet, 'and this is the way it will be again when we've finished covering that past with this present.'

The rhythmic lick of a paint brush some Saturday morning. The shaman chant of language.

Outside the bathroom window a summer breeze nods clumps of wild irises that grow thick along the back wall of the garden – open again and again – a pop and flutter of neon blue silk in the blink of summer after summer. In the far distance single-parent condominiums march ever closer – those empty apartments we will someday inhabit in our new beginnings. Each spring the same hawks that Yeats knew return to us, wheel their question marks in the sky overhead, nothing altering that sublime procession from one generation to the next except our forlorn methods of observation.

It is Nature that defends the unknown territories of the future I need to believe in.

The Present

As I wander along this ribbon of words the blue irises bend in a wind many months from now. There is no way for them to care about all the dreary bathrooms I've repainted, the empty apartments in strange cities that are waiting to frame my future. There must be a clearly focused first recollection simply because the present has come to depend on it.

First Memory

My first distinct recollection is of a tall hedge that I couldn't get through. It is a bright summer morning, the grass thick and wet as otter's fur. I can hear my mother's vacuum cleaner through the screen door on a back porch some twenty paces away.

Each day when I was put outside I made straight for that hedge – a boxwood hedge – until the clotheslines tethered to my chest harness brought me up short. There was a big open body of water on the other side of the hedge with a pier – a causeway, actually – running diagonally across it. In the summer my father anchored a huge army surplus raft offshore and spent all his free time down there hauling slabs of rock around, building a revetment wall to stop the slow erosion of our property into Lake Ontario. Or so he claims now. I have no idea what my dad was doing down there with that army surplus raft while I was securely tethered on the other side of the hedge. The actual memory I speak of with certainty here involves only the hedge, the drone of a vacuum cleaner through a distant screen door, the nodding concurrence of blue irises in an adjacent flower bed. To resolve the memory with a crisp image let's watch while Shaddrach, the neighbour's Labrador retriever, bounds into frame and trots up to lick my face. I fall to the seat of my pants, burst into tears. The vacuum cleaner groans to silence and my mother appears, a grainy 1949 silhouette captured in the frame of the screen door.

The next memory I can cleanly retrieve involves a Sunday afternoon birthday party for one of the kids who lived on the mink farm across the road. At least the adults told us it was a mink farm – those long, low buildings could have housed almost anything. For the sake of fiction let's call it a light switch factory. During a game of 'can't touch floor' at that birthday party I fell off the back porch and split my forehead open on the corner of a cinder block. My mom and dad rushed me off to emergency where a green intern sewed

the wound closed without the aid of an anaesthetic. A week later the sutures festered, grew tight with pus, leaving two dimpled scars high on my right temple. Sometimes I still notice them when I'm leaning close to the bathroom mirror to check the gradual recession of my hairline.

The point is, this monotonous inventory of recollection could go on indefinitely without significant result. The best memories have all been run dry in the service of the numberless forgeries that stand between me and my childhood. Time, like baseball, is a game of inches.

The Choreography of Recollection

According to Zeno's Paradox, a man who sets out to reach a wall by repeatedly halving his distance from it will finish his life shrieking on the head of a pin. Similarly, no list of memories – no matter how chronologically inclusive – will ever be long enough to connect my beginnings to the moment where I'm sitting now and the minds which made it possible.

The act of recollection is finally nothing more than an elegant ballroom exercise, our most graceful compulsory figure. The one no one else in the forest can do with us. In rare moments, when the dancer and the dance flow together, that part of us which longs to glide across time like Gene Kelly may find itself suddenly foot-loose in thc real world. As luck would have it, I'm presently equipped to offer a modest illustration of how one such unexpected, and seemingly insignificant, intersection of events set my dance in motion.

A moment ago something scratched my ankle and, reaching down, I realized I'd forgotten to remove a price tag stapled to one of the new wool sweat socks I purchased yesterday down in the city. I pulled off the tag, and in looking at it, was reminded that scarcely 24 hours ago a department store *pas de deux* helped me separate time from Time, the grey scales of fact from the black and white symmetry of Fiction.

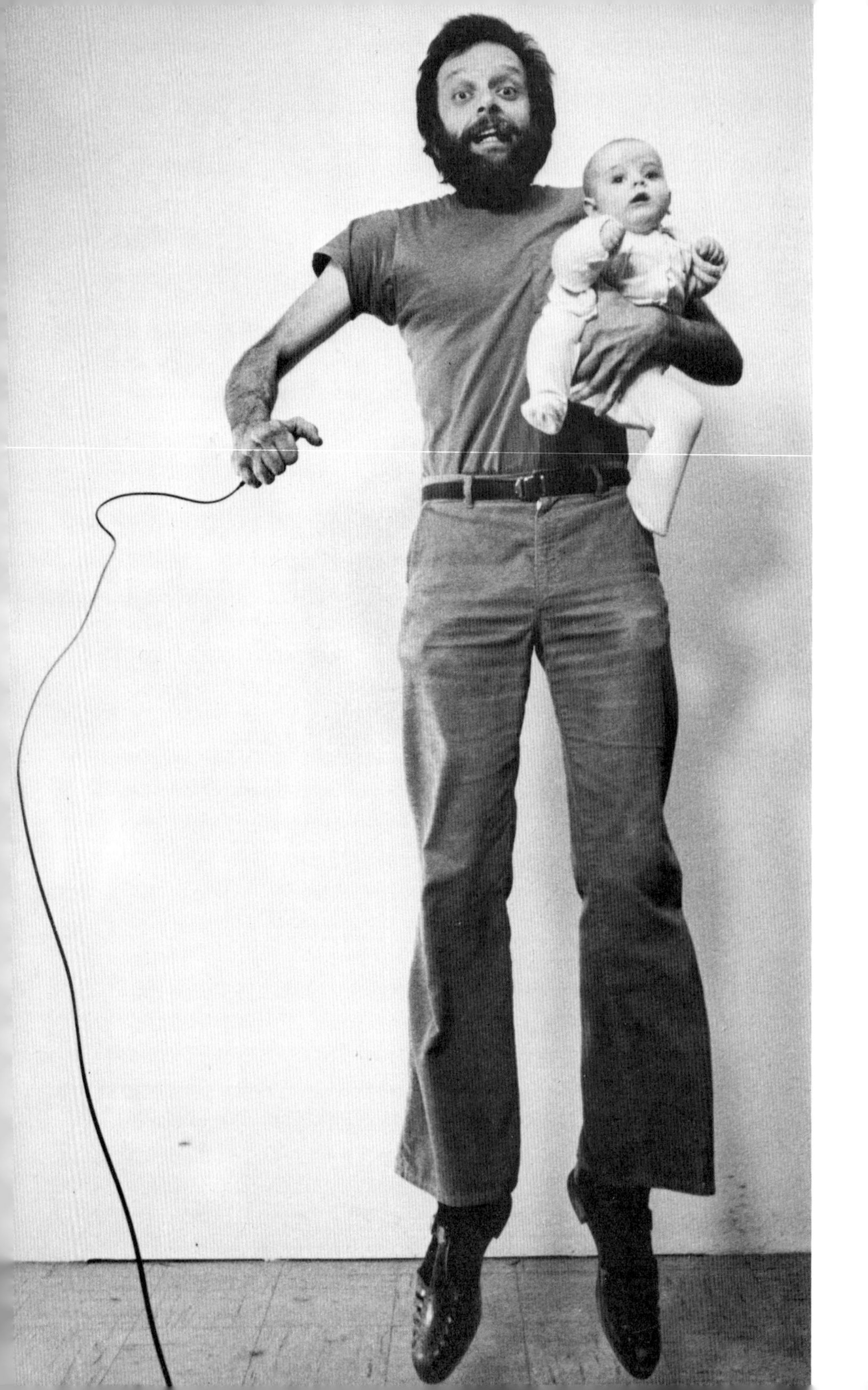

The Dancer & The Dance

The Dancer

At nine o'clock yesterday morning I pushed through revolving doors and entered a downtown department store. There wasn't another shopper in sight on the ground floor, just preoccupied clerks fussing with their display cases, idly waiting for the day to begin while Muzak wafted overhead.

I was standing at the top of the escalator on the second floor, wondering which way to go for wool sweat socks, when I caught sight of myself in a nearby mirror – one of those floor-to-ceiling jobs attached to a column. I stood still and studied my reflection, noticed nothing in particular except that I'd forgotten to comb my hair. Curiously, I felt my attention arrested nonetheless. A moment later I realized I wasn't so much looking, as *listening* – the high pitched whine of an electric motor somewhere nearby coming crisply into focus. The face in the mirror shifted a little, instinctively sensing that something in the air, a fragrance almost, was about to give my memory a place to dance. A dozen steps past my reflection stood the display cases of a perfume boutique – a partial explanation for the exotic fragrance ... yet ...

Yes.

Straight down the aisle in front of me stood an old-fashioned Hoover vacuum cleaner, its handle vertical – the engine hungrily sucking air. Instantly I knew I was hearing *exactly* the same model Hoover vacuum cleaner my mother had used in that house with the boxwood hedge. The clothesline tethered to my chest harness! The mysterious army surplus raft anchored offshore! I closed my eyes and let my body ground the memory charge – stayed like that until

I felt the tingle in my fingertips, then opened my eyes again.

The cord from the unattended Hoover came straight down the aisle toward me, then bent at 90° down a cross-aisle to my right and ran the width of the store to a distant wall socket. There was a big sign on the wall that said: EXCHANGES & REFUNDS. I looked at it for a moment, turning its meanings over and around until they connected with the way I was feeling, then tracked slowly back along the cord to the intersection of –

Thunder & lightning!

A salesgirl – a salesgirl! – stood with her back to me at the place where the Hoover's cord bent around the corner. I was absolutely *positive* she hadn't been there at the intersection of the aisles a moment earlier. Her sudden, solid presence was obviously the act of enchantment I'd been waiting for. I studied her, let my memory drift into associations that would anchor her in my past.

The salesgirl was of medium build, straight blonde hair cut blunt at the shoulder, arms crossed over her bosom, a tight black skirt and crisp white blouse accentuating the narrow cinch of her waist. She was tapping her foot to the Muzak that wafted overhead, her body swaying side to side ever so slightly. While I hadn't as yet seen her face, I knew that this salesgirl would be young, intelligent and devastatingly beautiful.

Strangely, she seemed entirely unaware of the whining vacuum cleaner – as if, in a playful mood, she hoped to convince me that her sudden materialization there at the intersection of the aisles had nothing whatever to do with my methods of recollection.

The Dance

I stayed where I was at the top of the escalator (in total I'd been there for perhaps a minute) – stood very still as I widened the frame of my focus. As I watched, the salesgirl casually lifted her right foot slightly off the floor, bent her knee a little and shuffled

her foot – a heel-toe, heel-toe move in tempo with the Muzak – then shifted her weight back onto her moving foot and repeated the shuffle with her other foot – ah-ha! There it was – the first clear acknowledgement of our conspiracy! She'd captured that vacuum cleaner's cord under the arch of her high heel!

An instant later the Hoover's whining engine moaned down to silence. With transparent guile the salesgirl pretended not to notice the change – a coy and petulant disinterest worthy of Leslie Caron. Her tactic pleased me and I left her to refine it, ran my attention back along the cord to – *yes,* the plot thickened! A black man in a green janitor's uniform was squatting by the wall socket, the Hoover's disconnected plug in his hand. As I watched, the black man came to his feet and began to saunter down the aisle toward me, rhythmically looping the cord into the palm of his hand, his attitude loose and street-wise.

I returned my attention to the salesgirl, still facing away from me on her spot at the junction of the aisles. The Muzak score was clearer now without the whine of that vacuum cleaner. I recognized the tune of *Me & My Shadow* as the salesgirl began to sway deliberately with the tempo, tapping the toe of her right shoe emphatically now. The salesgirl's mind seemed far away, perhaps crossing private distances to refine the last detail of some pleasing memory before the first customers arrived. Toying with our telepathy, I focused her dreamy reminiscence. Visualized a horizon of open water dissected by a pier – a causeway, actually – a backyard thick with wild irises, the sweet smell of a week-old paint job rekindled by rushing steam when she and her new man took happy showers after making love in their favourite dawn moment. She flexed her shoulders and arched her back in response to my lead.

Meanwhile, the black maintenance man padded down the aisle toward the place where she stood. He seemed cool and unconcerned as the coils of cord grew thick in the palm of his hand. Neither of them had as yet formally acknowledged me on my spot

The Nikon

by the fake rubber tree at the top of the escalator. Even if they had, it would've been easy enough to mistake me for a mannequin temporarily misplaced en route to Sportswear – this pose of absolute passivity being essential to that Gene Kelly tap-shuffle-strut across time which seemed mere moments away. I stood perfectly still, studying the choreography, waiting for my cue.

A dozen feet from the intersection of the aisles the black maintenance man gently laid his coiled cord on the tile floor and padded silently onward. He approached the salesgirl from behind, as if this time he really had a good one up his sleeve – his stalking approach perfectly in synch with the mood of my observation.

As if commanded by baton, the Muzak stopped, the mush of strings interrupted by the disembodied voice of a woman, one of those thin, machine-made voices you hear in hospital corridors:

Mr Phipps? Mr Phipps, please? Mr Phipps to the west-end shop ...

During this announcement, the black maintenance man knelt, careful as a cat in the grass, slightly behind the motionless salesgirl, remained there, poised, as the announcement echoed off across the deserted display areas. It was obvious that the salesgirl didn't know that a black man in a green janitor's uniform crouched behind her cradling the vacuum cleaner cord that ran under her feet. When the Muzak tape cut back in she began to tap her foot again in time to another billowing melody. At this point the black man's mute strategy became even more mysterious. Instead of announcing himself as I'd expected, he held his motionless crouch and surreptitiously slipped the fingertips of his right hand under the salesgirl's tapping toe.

In a flash all that was cool suddenly shifted to hot, then *hotter* than hot! As the patent leather tip of the salesgirl's shoe continued to tap a slow, steady rhythm on the fingertips of the black maintenance man's hand I felt my imagination start to sweat. Had the moment been sustainable I knew that black man would happily have knelt like that all day, basking in the salesgirl's fragrant aura, that

perfume of my childhood, the cord he held connecting us both to a mother's breast. Time stood still – my cue! Bold with my sense of the moment, I entered the tableau, hoping to alter its shape before events hardened into language.

'Excuse me, Miss – I'm looking for sweat socks?'

In the same instant both of them turned, saw me, then each other. The salesgirl hopped back, as if startled by a mild electric shock. She shook her head, nonplussed, while the black maintenance man rose laughing to his feet and exclaimed: 'Lord knows, I been *waiting*, Sarah! I thought maybe this bea -*oo*-tiful lady decided to pretend her old friend Emile got himself *invisible*! Thank you, Sarah! Thank you, Miss Duke!'

The salesgirl and I exchanged non-committal smiles. She really was beautiful.

'Sweat socks?'

'Uh-huh.'

The salesgirl named Sarah Duke directed me to Sportswear on the third floor, blinked a couple of times. There was a click, as if a photograph was being taken.

'Do I know you?'

'I don't think so,' I said, 'why?'

'Because you're looking at me like I should.'

I shook my head, shrugged apologetically, as our smiles deepened, the two of us coding the moment for permanent storage as we backed away from each other, probably for good.

What was it all about? I have no idea. We are left with a Hoover vacuum cleaner, a dreaming salesgirl named 'Sarah Duke' who could be a stranger, or my mother, or a girlfriend whose future I may someday embrace in the fragrant steam of a freshly-painted bathroom.

The Last Beginning

Perhaps the single most important statement I can make about my childhood is that, in the summer of my sixth year, the focus of everything changed with abrupt and utter certainty. In those days a wind of savage power came suddenly into the treetops. It blew relentlessly for months, frightening the adults. Far to the north, wildcat prospectors hit the mother-lode of the century, a towering mountain of high-grade uranium! In June, the King slipped into a coma and, a month later, a herd of cows in Devon started giving dark green milk. Confused and dispirited, my parents' generation bolted into open panic, began hoarding canned goods and memorizing government pamphlets that explained how to seal off the basement windows with wet towels while the kids built a fort under the dining room table with blankets and pillows. In the spare moments between tension and worry they shopped with a vengeance.

In the midst of this monumental disturbance my parents presented me with a miniature replica of a man's fedora for my sixth birthday. It is with this seemingly inconsequential acquisition that everything which was to follow began.

1600

Heart of My Heart

The Mind's Body

Sunday afternoon. Winter. I lie in bed, drifting with the pleasant euphoria of a slight fever. Outside the window grey monochromatic light shifts toward evening. I can hear the grown-ups talking in the next room. They're trying to carry on serious cocktail-hour conversations while my brother and sister squeal and squabble, wrestling over toys, chasing each other out of the room and upstairs, their feet bumping on the ceiling above my bed until they slide back down along spokes of bright laughter. Cooking smells from the kitchen. I lift the blanket over my head and look into the eerie amber interior of the tent the heat lamp's frame suspends over my lower legs. The air inside the tent is hot and sweetly pungent. Below the knee my right leg is tight and puffy, the afternoon's application of pink salve dried and cracking along the shin, curls of yellow skin sloughing off the tips of my toes like old porch paint. I roll slightly to study the sunken ulcers on the outside of my leg, one just above the bump of my ankle bone, the other in the middle of my calf muscle a few inches below the knee. Both of the puckered craters are open and glistening with the poison the doctors say the heat lamp will draw. I enjoy looking into the tent like this, calculating the slow putrefaction of my leg in response to the attack of various procedures and medications. Sometimes at night the leg throbs a little, calling into my dream, and when I surface and peek under the tent I feel quiet pride because, despite its gruesome appearance, my bad leg doesn't hurt at all, *ever.* All I have to do is treat it objectively, as if it belongs to someone else.

My mother enters the next room and turns on the lights and my

brother says something that makes all the adults laugh. My father puts on a Dixieland jazz record and one of the guests, Mrs Mumford from across the street, asks if he'll play some of their old favourites on the banjo after dinner. My dad says sure and Mrs Mumford bubbles with excitement, singing and humming a chorus of *Heart of My Heart* while my mother swishes around the room again to freshen the drinks one last time before the group goes into the dining room for Sunday supper. Meanwhile, Mr Lumb's voice has risen into a story he wants my father to hear.

Earl Lumb is one of my dad's most important clients – a Virginia contractor involved in the natural gas pipeline they're building across Northern Ontario. Whenever he and his wife come over for Sunday dinner we children are expected to be on our best behaviour. Lately, I'd become the star performer for all these occasions, showing the guests how bright and brave I could be while they looked at the bad leg hinged to my body at the right knee. Based on the foreign meat's smell and appearance the guests invariably presumed I was in considerable pain, perhaps depressed beyond my years because I couldn't run and jump like the other kids. People like the Lumbs usually responded to this disturbing situation by giving me get-well cards with fresh ten dollar bills scotch-taped inside. I'd read the cards aloud, smile and say thanks while I unstuck the money – not bothering to tell them the truth, which was that I felt absolutely no pain and, in fact, had become rather attached to the bargain my bad leg allowed me to strike with the world of adults. When it came time to leave, the guests would tussle my hair and tell me I was one heckuva brave young fella, which made me happier still – euphoric in fact – as I strained to listen in while they compared notes on the progress of my disease out in the hall.

The Luminous Fall

Mr Lumb finished telling his anecdote about the old days in the Merchant Marine, and my father laughed energetically. My brother and sister laughed too, waiting for my father to stop laughing before they stopped laughing. A moment later my mother announced that dinner was on the table and the room next door grew quiet as the voices of the adults receded down the hall. I'd told my mum I didn't want dinner until later so there'd be at least an hour – more than enough time for me to visit my hide-out.

The fire in the next room snapped and popped against the screen. I focused my eyes on the luminous face of the alarm clock on the dresser across the room – zoomed in on the circular shape until the lime green numerals and the intervening glow of the minute strokes broke free in the velvet darkness and began to float. Pulled my focus in further until my vision formed a fish-eye tunnel, let the face of the clock come inside the tunnel and drift toward me ... thought about the tough older kids who set up pins at the bowling alley and smoked Buckingham straights under the willow tree at the far end of the school yard. Thought about my godfather who did push-ups and sit-ups before breakfast every day – the way his back muscles pulsed with the exertion – my godfather always arriving late for Sunday dinner wearing grubby clothes – later than usual tonight ... but ... the lamp's heat, a counterfeit summer, my bad leg sealed inside a plastic bag so I could dangle it in Georgian Bay, the water sluicing transparent sheets up and over the granite loaf of shore. My mum claimed Georgian Bay rocks were the oldest in the world, towering volcanoes polished to nubs by the rhythmic advance and retreat of glaciers.

A pale throb the heat lamp was welding to my body ... draw the glowing face of the clock closer, almost touch the sound with the tip of my nose – voices miles away, laughter momentarily spiking from the skin of yet another family telling in which I would play no part. Fumes from the melting salve, wild flowers on a humid night, a tent out on the prairie somewhere illuminated from within.

The Deserted Battlefield

I went inside the tent, sat down in front of an old Indian, olive-skinned and deeply lined, like the *National Geographic* Navajo I'd seen in the afternoon. Outside the tent a night dog coughed and growled. The distant thump of Dixieland jazz from a nearby settlement. I offered the old Indian my attention and he touched my bad leg, instantly reducing it to normal size and coloration. Then he carefully opened a leather pouch on the dirt floor and pointed to a snapshot from my childhood mounted inside it, cocking his forehead toward me, waiting for the expression on my face to change. I opened my eyes slightly to pull the face of the clock further in, moved the luminous dial up toward the lighter water near the surface of the tank. Sensing the shift in my attention, the old man lifted the pouch into his lap and began to examine the photographs individually, no longer letting me see what he was seeing. Distant laughter echoed again across the prairie night and I suddenly saw myself as a forlorn reveller in the far corner of some deserted battlefield. I tried to open my eyes, couldn't, thought: 'But why a *battlefield*?'

The old man looked suddenly tired. 'Because,' he whispered, examining the photographs one by one, his voice careful with its fatigue, 'Because that is the nature of our self-obsession.'

The old man's face opened in a bright easy smile, his laughter was a kettle of wonderful shining fishes.

Medicated Jello

I awake in darkness, confused by the old man's smile. Any minute now my mother will bring in a tray with roast beef done just the way I like it, then practically applaud from the doorway while I poke it with my fork. As soon as I've finished the dish of medicated jello which accompanies all my meals, she and dad will bustle back into the adjoining room, cleaning ashtrays and collecting empty glasses until it's time for us to be our very happiest together, shattering the mirror of the day as we say goodnights. Bodies telescoping away toward an idea called tomorrow.

ARMY

Gilbert & Sullivan vs Tom & Jerry

Droppings

One spring my parents gave my brother and me matching yellow canaries, this after the two of us, in a rare moment of agreement, had asked to have a jointly-owned pet parrot which we might teach to say certain things. As it was, the idea of canaries fulfilled some powerful childhood longing for my mother so my brother and I took the change of species in stride and put the two identical cages opposite each other in the playroom. According to the brochure that accompanied our pet canaries this slight distancing would encourage the male and female – we never could tell the difference – to serenade each other when they were 'in season.'

It was my mother who named our birds Gilbert & Sullivan. On a return trip to the pet shop she even bought them an instructional l.p. – spectacular mating melodies sung by the world's top-pedigree canaries. Boy, was my mum excited about those birds!

For the first little while it was kind of fun to service our canaries, topping up the little porcelain seed and water dishes, changing the wax paper on the removable bottom trays after the gravel became soiled with their pasty droppings. It was especially neat to drape the cloth over their cages and know they'd have their heads tucked under their wings in two minutes even if it was still broad daylight outside. In the brochure it said Gilbert & Sullivan would take a couple of weeks to get used to the way my brother and I managed their daily routines – then they'd start to sing like crazy.

The weeks passed, became months, and our pet canaries rarely moved on their perches, much less sang. In fact, those little varmints never made any kind of noise, even if you strummed your thumbnail along the bars of their cages. If you weren't the one who changed the wax paper on their bottom trays every forty-eight hours you might well have thought Gilbert & Sullivan deft forgeries of polished wax.

Some time in the final days of that summer my mum began to nag my brother and me about keeping our canary cages clean. In truth, we had begun to let the cages go for a week here, ten days there, giving Gilbert & Sullivan plenty of time to kick all of their Hartz Mountain feed onto the carpet and run their water dishes bone dry before we got around to the increasingly bothersome chore. In short order clean canary cages became a stipulated condition for all parental agreements about who was going where, and for how long. And so it was that on more than a few sunny autumn afternoons Gilbert & Sullivan stood between my brother and me and a game of 'touchy blues' in the park or sucker spearing in the shallows along the shoreline of the lake.

Sometime in late October my brother unaccountably broke with standard maintenance procedures and began letting Gilbert fly free around the room while he serviced the bird's cage. He claimed he did this to strengthen the bond of trust between him and his pet. During one of these free-flying sessions the inevitable happened – Gilbert buzzed around in tight circles until he'd picked up a full head of steam, then streaked the length of the room and tried to blast his way out through the picture window. He hit the plate glass head-on, pinwheeled to the carpet and lay there, inert, his head screwed around at a crazy angle. His little talons clenched twice, and were still.

My brother, never one to openly display his inner emotions, held himself tightly in check. He'd dealt with the loss of pets before – a turtle, a hamster and a half-grown beagle puppy lay buried side by side in the far corner of our backyard. For him it was a time to deal quietly and forthrightly with harsh realities – a Jackie Kennedy approach to grief. He placed Gilbert's little corpse in a quart basket full of excelsior, covered it with foil wrap and performed a solemn burial ceremony in the backyard cemetery while my mum and I watched from the upstairs balcony.

Indy Pit Stops

In the weeks that followed my brother frequently spoke sadly about the departed Gilbert, expressing the hope that, with proper care, Sullivan might enjoy a long and melodious life despite his mate's untimely passing.

October wore on into November and Sullivan, sullen and doubly-silent now, began to cut deeper into the foreshortened hours of daylight between school and supper. When my mother, ever the cheerful optimist, put on the record of famous canary performances Sullivan would freeze on his perch, his tiny black eyes staring unfocused into some prehistoric distance – stay like that for days, not even bothering to eat, nothing moving except those little tail feathers that periodically tipped up to signal another bowel movement. Predictably, my brother continued to take a proprietary interest in the remaining canary, promptly notifying my mum whenever he felt the conditions inside Sullivan's cage were becoming less than sanitary. No way that canary of mine was going to open his heart and sing if his cage was filthy.

As November passed I did my best to keep Sullivan comfortable. Grimly, I refined a series of short-cuts that allowed me to pull out the bottom tray, whap the canary shit onto a sheet of newspaper, slap in a pre-cut circle of clean wax paper, reach up into the cage with both hands to retrieve the seed and water dishes, refill them with fluid scooping motions down into two waiting quart tins, a follow-through rhythm carrying the porcelain dishes back up into the cage where I locked them into place with a snap of the wrists, then, spinning at the waist, I'd retrieve the bottom tray, whirl around and – *BAM-CLANG!* – it was back in place and I was done,

leaping away with my hands in the air like a triumphant rodeo rider – 14.3 seconds! Those Indy-style pit stops were such a blur that Sullivan didn't even have time to look down and get interested in what he might do with that gaping hole I'd left under his perch. I'm absolutely positive that if someone had organized a province-wide competition for youngsters with silent canaries I'd have made it at least to the Regionals. Maybe nudged out of further competition by a little Rumanian girl who'd been given her first silent canary at the age of three. Eight seconds flat, start to finish, and the commentator'd have to run her routine back and forth in slow motion when he explained how she did it.

I think I was just a little past my peak times the day it happened. A split-second after I'd whipped the bottom tray out from under him Sullivan dove head-first through the hole – he didn't even flap his wings! – and was instantly swatted out of the air by Perkins, my sister's twenty-pound Persian cat, who vanished under the couch with my pet canary clamped in her jaws. I dove after Perkins and desperately tried to squeeze under there past the fluff, marbles and broken crayons – ready to do anything to free poor Sullivan before his frantic peeping stopped.

All in vain.

I, more sensitive and emotionally open than my brother, could not be consoled for many hours. I just went off by myself out there on the lawn in front of the kitchen window and sat hunched up and sniffling for the whole afternoon. My mum brought me out a jelly sandwich on a plate but I didn't even look at it.

At dusk that day I prepared Sullivan for interment in the backyard pet cemetery beside Gilbert – the quart basket full of excelsior, the tin foil, the popsicle stick cross dated in pencil. I had the grave half-dug when my brother approached. I noticed he was carrying the new Slazenger badminton racquet he'd received for his birthday. Sensing my attention, he darted ahead and, without asking permission, took Sullivan's corpse from the bier, lofted it over his head, and *poinged* the little body high over the hedge into the neighbour's yard. I stood there, stunned and speechless, jerked my arm away when my brother tried to explain how funny all of it was. I refused to make peace with him until he'd helped me follow through with the charade of burying the empty casket and promised that he'd never, *ever* tell my mother.

My brother kept his oath of silence until about half-way through dinner that night. Then he blurted it out, the whole burial story, telling it as if the badminton racquet had been entirely my idea, as if he, the *innocent* bystander, had merely come along to watch me whap Sullivan's corpse over the hedge into the neighbour's yard. Unbelievable! The lying bastard! Naturally, I tried to counter his totally distorted version of the episode with the real facts, but my dad and my brother kept interrupting my corrections with their relentless laughter. Finally I gave up.

My mother, silent and expressionless, put down her knife and fork and stared at me from the other side of the dining room table.

The Concentration Camp

The Favourites

In 1956 I was in grade five at Riverside public school, a sickly ten-year-old, I imagine now, fresh out of hospital after a time-consuming bout with osteomyelitis. Our class that year was split between grades five and six, about thirty-five kids in all, and Mr Hubble was our teacher.

The first precise detail I remember about Mr Hubble was that he drove a lemon yellow DKW, a funny looking German car shaped like a Volkswagen with missing chromosomes. The second thing I remember is that he claimed he was related to Vic Hubble who played for the New York Rangers. Then his appearance: rail-thin and gawky as a flamingo. Mr Hubble brylcreemed his thick black hair in an Eddy Byrnes flat-top, the extra long side pieces of his ducktail frequently coming unstuck to frame his face like an Afghan's ears – thick dandruff building up from week to week on the lapels of the shapeless blazer he wore to school every day. While he couldn't have been more than twenty-five, Mr Hubble seemed much older – his face a downward droop of washed-out Modigliani despair, the blue-black rings around his eyes suggesting some secret suffering. His normal speaking voice was high and reedy, tremulous with a kind of false excitement that made him stutter and stammer. Flecks of white foam would gather in the corners of his mouth spritzing the front rows when he emphasized the key points of a lesson under the high lathe ceiling of that red brick schoolhouse they'd tear down and replace before I graduated from grade eight in '59.

Everyone's had a teacher who looks and acts like Mr Hubble. But there's more to it than that.

Mr Hubble had a couple of noteworthy habits that set him apart from every other teacher I ever had – although not, by any means, from *all* teachers. These habits had to do with the way he treated some of the kids in the class. To put it bluntly, Mr Hubble 'played favourites' and to be one of Mr Hubble's favourites was, in the snapshot of that age, a unique and nameless experience. Precisely what did it involve? I will tell you, precisely.

If you happened to be one of Mr Hubble's favourites, and his favourites were only boys, perhaps four of us in all, then you could expect to be regularly summoned to 'show your work' while the rest of the class went on quietly with new assignments. When it was my turn – normally about once a week – I'd go to the front of the class and stand beside Mr Hubble while he leafed through my Hilroy notebook, gave it a close reading and asked questions in a confidential whisper. While Mr Hubble reviewed my work he'd insist that I stand close by his chair and pay strict attention to his every utterance. He backed up this insistence by holding me in place at the waist with his right hand while he licked the first finger of his left hand to turn the pages and show me where I'd gone wrong in my exercises, or what was done particularly well.

Imagine a spider.

At some point in this closely choreographed routine Mr Hubble began gently tugging at the back of my shirt until the tails came untucked. First one cool finger, then another, would snake under, grazing the flesh of my lower back. After a few minutes of this cat and mouse, Mr Hubble would use the easy conviviality of something that pleased him in my workbook to boldly slide his right hand fully under my shirt. That's when the real fun started.

All the other favourites scattered around in their rows, instinc-

tively aware that Hubble had completed his docking manoeuvre, would start twisting their faces into grotesque masks trying to make me laugh, or better yet blush with the effort of suppressing laughter. The other favourites knew that if anyone made even a tiny sound Mr Hubble would react instantly, look up and around the room like a cobra. It was extremely dangerous to make eye contact with him during those moments. His temper was hair-triggered and lava hot – once provoked he was in no way afraid to give it full expression. He could slam a yardstick across a desk so hard that the noise made you bawl. In view of the risks the other favourites proceeded with great care, never stopping the movement of their pencils as they flashed cross-eyed gargoyle expressions up from the page, and instantly back down. At the same time Mr Hubble, perhaps sensing the battle for control, used his massaging right hand as best he could to hold my attention.

I stood there like that, pressed close to Mr Hubble's side, air sweet with his pomade. The classroom took on a telescoped distance, the clanking mutter and hiss of the rads marking time as pencils moved back and forth along the light blue rules of thirty-five Hilroy scribblers. At some point in this hallucination it would be like I was looking down from the ceiling while Mr Hubble used some casual remark to edge a surreptitious baby finger under the elasticized waistband of my corduroys. In the telepathy of that moment all the other favourites knew that the critical threshold had been crossed and immediately put their heads down on their desks, feigning infinite concentration. They no longer tried to make me laugh. The enterprise had become far too dangerous.

For a minute or two, perhaps only the time it takes to fall from a high stepladder, I hung there alone – a snagged catfish circling to the surface – while Mr Hubble finished reviewing my workbook and tested the boundaries of my last encounter with his wandering right hand.

At recess, we favourites would huddle in the schoolyard and

compare notes: What *exactly* had Hubble said in his muttering way to cover the various thresholds? How had he choreographed the crux move down onto bare ass? Was the penetration a new record or merely a confidence-building rerun of the last encounter? And, most important, who'd come closest to making you totally crack up and twist away, your uncontrollable shriek igniting the cold and pitiless laughter we all bravely imagined and planned together?

Of course, those outside the circle of favourites knew what we were talking about in a vague sort of way, but they never shared our direct understanding of the experience. Especially the girls in the class. It was obvious that Mr Hubble had trouble relating to girls, except for Sarah Duke – the very brightest and prettiest in the class. He seemed almost to crave Sarah Duke's approval, had her sit behind his desk as class monitor whenever he had to run down to the office. When he wasn't sure of a fact it was always Sarah Duke who got to check in the encyclopedia. She was the only one who could bring his secret memories to life.

Prickly Heat

In the fall of 1956 I wrote a short story for Mr Hubble about the events inside a German concentration camp on the day it was liberated. All I can remember of that composition now is that I used the word 'grisly' to describe the shards of skull Allied troops discovered when they poked the ashes with their rifle butts.

Mr Hubble liked my short story so much that he read it aloud to the whole class. He said it was the best composition he'd ever seen – which was unexpected since I'd so recently returned from an eighteen-month absence and was well behind the others. Actually, I can admit it now, I lifted that concentration camp story word for word from an article I'd read in *TRUE MAGAZINE*. (I used to worship *TRUE*, savouring it from cover to cover every month – all those Japs, Nazis, Wops and terrier-sized rats squirming and slobbering on top of each other. The cover story always featuring some fetid torture-pit where jack-booted sluts applied red hot knitting needles to Joe Palooka, and came up wanting – our boys storming in with guns that went *buddha-buddha-buddha* at the last possible moment.)

A few days after he'd read my concentration camp story aloud Mr Hubble suggested, in front of the entire class, that I be nominated to stay after school and help him render the human digestive system on the side board in preparation for our next science topic. All the other favourites immediately realized that this was a whole new ball game. Getting an ass massage in front of thirty-five other kids was one thing. Going one-on-one after school when there was nobody else around except old Jarko Osbourne sweeping that green shit up and down the halls? Christ, next thing you knew Hubble and I'd be going on weekend canoe trips.

As the big solo approached I tried to keep my cool amid rampant recess speculation from the other favourites. That last afternoon I quietly asked D'arcy Hodges, my next door neighbour and best friend, to *promise* that he'd hang around in the schoolyard until Hubble was done with me. At the final bell I was panicky, yet unaccountably curious – caught in a crossfire of strange emotions which are precise in memory to this day.

After the rest of the kids had filed through the cloakroom and clumped downstairs – headed home for afternoon cartoons – Mr Hubble took off his blue blazer and hung it on the back of a chair he dragged across the room for me to stand on. Mr Hubble helped me up and suggested that I begin with the mouth and esophagus. While I translated the shape and scale of the digestive system from a textbook held at waist level in my left hand Mr Hubble stood beside me, the top of his head at my shoulder. He followed my rendering in his own textbook, offering quiet bits of advice here and there. The esophagus was a little too long, I'd distorted the curve of the stomach, the first crenellation of the duodenum.

Room dead quiet. Only hissing rads.

Mr Hubble didn't touch me or even stand close to me while I sketched my way down past the stomach. I could tell he knew exactly how I was feeling.

Then, for no apparent reason, he stopped following the slow progress of my drawing and started to talk again about the concentration camp story, stepping back from the blackboard as I changed to green chalk and began to wiggle around the s-curve of the large intestine. Mr Hubble said my short story had reminded him of himself. The way he'd seen the world when he was young and misunderstood, a lad who made wonderful things even though there was nobody around to understand and encourage him. The war had blown his family apart. They'd arrived in Canada utterly disoriented in their flight from the phantom squads of the Ukraine. As I continued my cross-section of the large intestine, Mr. Hubble began to talk in detail about his childhood, made me promise that everything we said would be private. Just between the two of us. It had to be that way. Most of the people out there didn't understand how it was for people like him and me. He said my short story made him feel like we were brothers – it was so wonderful to finally be *with* someone who understood!

Mr Hubble went on in his high sing-song about the elements of my concentration camp story which had had special meaning for him – how he could tell they came from my own inner circumstances and that I shouldn't worry because it was *alright.* Everything was going to be just *fine.* I wasn't *alone* any more.

I could smell his pomade, feel heat prickling up the backs of my legs, alarm rising to fog my eyes. At some point I stopped trying to understand what Mr Hubble was talking about, lost my place in the diagram and left out an entire section of the small intestine as I

hurried to finish my drawing before Mr Hubble said any more about why I reminded him of himself – a young boy who did private things that no one else understood.

Suddenly he stopped telling his story, which was his version of my story, and came to my side, lightly touching the calf of my left leg with the fingertips of his left hand as he pointed out that I'd missed an entire section of the small intestine and might as well erase back to the stomach and try it over again.

Splat!

My textbook hit the floor and I was in tears – sobbing uncontrollably with my arms at my sides. Mr Hubble's face was a mask of confused amazement. He acted as if he had no idea what was going on as he squeezed my hands and stared up at me. What was going on? What was the matter? I was crying too hard to talk and all I could manage to blubber was that it was getting late and I couldn't finish the diagram of the human digestive system and I wanted to go home. Mr Hubble helped me off the chair and sat me down at one of the front desks until my breathing caught up with my crying, repeating over and over again that I was his *very best* student and I shouldn't worry about catching up with the other kids because I didn't *need* to catch up.

As soon as I'd calmed down Mr Hubble told me I could go home as soon as I promised I'd come and talk to him right away if I ever had this kind of confidence problem again.

D'arcy Hodges was waiting for me in the schoolyard. As soon as he saw how I looked he quit joking around, just walked alongside me and listened while I sketched the episode between hiccups and sniffles.

I was pretty steady by the time we got home and never mentioned the incident to my mom and dad.

160
confirmation

Sexual Torque

In the last week before Christmas Mr Hubble gave a grade six girl named Irene Thompson the slugs in front of the whole class. Irene Thompson was not a good or promising student. Her face was overly round, confused in every expression except apathy. Her mother kept her in ribbons and flounces – like she was a robot designed for birthday parties. Above all else, Irene Thompson was one of the worst talkers in our class. Catching her passing a note that final day, Mr Hubble went completely berserk, seized her by the wrists, dragged her to the front of the class and twisted her arm into a hammerlock while he threw open all his desk drawers looking for the strap. Irene Thompson shrieked and pummelled, demanding his peak effort. For a moment, it almost seemed like Mr Hubble had forgotten the rest of us were watching.

His savage strapping left purple welts on both of Irene Thompson's forearms, injuries serious enough to send her down to the nurse's office, then home for the rest of the day. The following morning Mr Hubble was gone.

The pimply young substitute teacher who came in to cover our lessons that first week said only that Mr Hubble had asked to be relieved so he could go out west to visit his dad who was seriously ill. When snickers rippled around the room the guy was at least honest enough to turn red while he frowned.

The following week a lady teacher named Iris White took over our class. Miss White was young and raven haired, a robustly attractive farmer's daughter with beautiful high breasts that we glimpsed periodically, the bulging cones of a snow white brassiere winking behind the open middle button of her starched blouses.

We boys waited, and waited, dreaming, ever hopeful, but Iris White never once chose favourites, much less tugged a shirt-tail loose to fondle bare bum. Pity – it would have given this account a

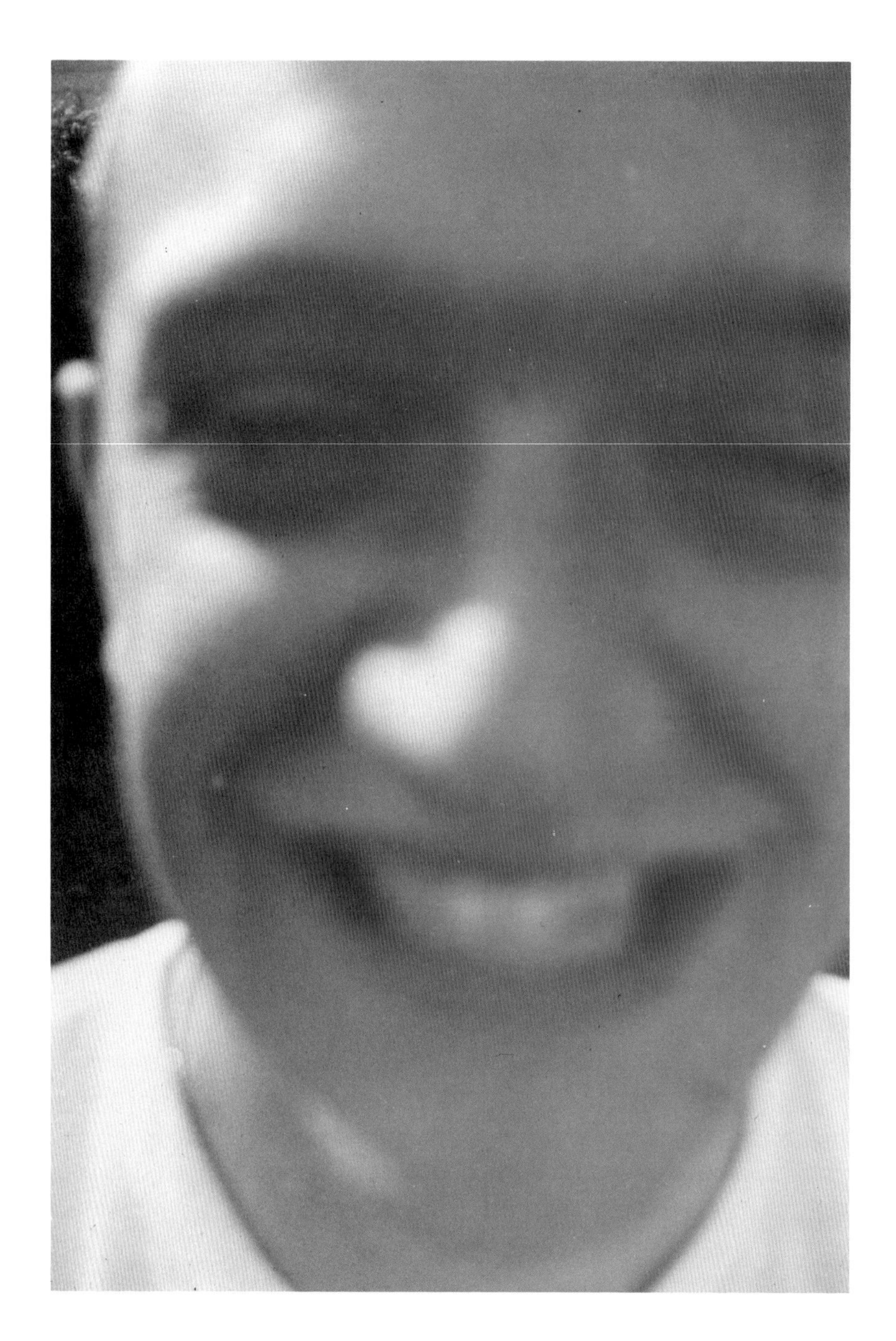

sexual torque worthy of *TRUE MAGAZINE*. Perhaps some day the primitive obsessions of men and women will be perfectly symmetrical. Perhaps someday newspapers will cost a nickel. In the meantime, Mr Hubble, no doubt suffering still somewhere beyond this cabin window, consider yourself forgiven.

Three Falls

Toenails

I first saw Emile Hops, or Toenails as he came to be called, when they put him in our grade seven class at Riverside public school. What a strange apparition! He was a tall, raw-boned kid with snow-capped pimples all over his face, greasy black hair that stood straight up in a cowlick, silky fuzz on his top lip, and an overly loud voice, a honk really, that cracked in stammers when he stood at the front of the class that first morning to introduce himself as a newcomer from Moncton, New Brunswick.

As Emile Hops lurched down the aisle toward the empty seat behind me, my classmates buzzed and tittered excitedly. This new guy looked almost old enough to be somebody's dad! Naturally, Mr Carrie didn't have to explain that Emile Hops was 'a slow learner.' Although it was always polite to pretend otherwise, in our herd cripples and fools brought up the rear.

Even so, Emile Hops did add a rather startling texture to the familiar routines of our classroom. For instance, the way he blurted out answers without putting up his hand or even lifting his head off his desk. The main crop in Saskatchewan? 'Booze for the rustlers!' he'd sing out gaily, laughing too loud and too long while the rest of us indicated with sidelong glances that we found him, what was the word, *exotic*.

It's difficult to say what would have happened to Emile Hops – how he would have earned his nickname and found his place among us – if I, nominated as schoolyard host, hadn't introduced him that first afternoon to Dean Sharp, the grade-eighter in charge of knockouts.

A Cavern under the Schoolyard

Knockout was a clandestine recess ritual that'd somehow migrated to our school yard earlier that fall from the Catholic kids who attended St Agnes on the other side of the highway. The procedure was dead simple. At recess one of the older boys would publicly offer himself to Dean Sharp as a candidate for the next knockout session. Within minutes there'd be a swarm of us under the big willow tree behind the catcher's cage of the lower baseball diamond. Once the grade-eighters had manhandled us small fry into a circle the volunteer would take his place in the open space at the centre – stand there like Kirk Douglas waiting for the lion. When everything was ready, Sharpie, serious and deliberate, would approach his subject, grip him firmly around the chest from behind and hold on tight while the volunteer took a rapid series of deep, even breaths, continuing a vigorous hyper-ventilation until the older kids started a countdown. Five! ... Four! ... Three! Two! One! GO! Whereupon the volunteer tried to expell the last molecules of oxygen from his lungs the same instant that Dean Sharp administered a ferocious chest squeeze from behind. A moment later the volunteer lost consciousness and fell limp to the ground.

For a moment we stood absolutely still, a tableau of Pre-Raphaelite silence. Then the volunteer would twitch and our circle would press in eagerly around him – attentive as New Guinea tribesmen studying a Polaroid picture – the slack face, the rolled-back whites of the eyes. When we clustered in too tight the grade-eighters would shove us back, hollering: 'C'mon, dorks! Give'm some air! Can't you see the guy needs AIR?'

After about ten seconds the volunteer would slowly loll onto an elbow and blink his eyes, clearly dumbfounded by all of us. Then, while we heartily cheered his adventure, he'd stand unsteadily with

the assistance of the other big kids before a teacher caught wind of our commotion from the front steps of the school and hustled down to investigate. On the way back we'd all be trying to walk alongside him, the courageous one, clamouring: 'What was it *like*? What'd you SEE?'

'Like I was watching myself get smaller and smaller down a tunnel,' he'd say, or 'It was all bright white and I heard echoes,' always saving the most intimate details for Dean Sharp, the ringleader, who'd earned everyone's respect by being the first to venture alone into that mysterious cavern under our schoolyard.

Real Vomit

By the time Emile Hops arrived at the school the original four adventurers had, each in turn, passed through the eye of the knockout ritual perhaps half a dozen times. All except for Sharpie, who liked to maintain his prestige by staying a few trips ahead of his pals. We little kids formed an enthusiastic and adoring audience, eagerly encouraging the original four grade-eighters to narrow the time lag between demonstrations, all the while being careful to stay well out of arm's reach ourselves. As long as Dean Sharp stayed at least one knockout session ahead and showed no ill effects the others seemed willing enough to take their places in the orderly rotation. Before long the schedule had settled down to one knockout session a week, with afternoon recess on Friday the preferred time slot.

All of this came unstuck in early November when Dean Sharp got himself excused from a spelling test by puking on the floor beside his desk. A clever trick? With Sharpie you could never be sure. In the course of flunking grades seven and eight he'd mastered the art of the off-beat alibi, knew a dozen ways to con his way into the nurse's office so he could cop a few zzz's while the rest of us wrote tests. But this time it was different. That'd been real puke on the

floor and he'd actually *fainted* outside in the hall!

Later that day Phipps did his best to laugh the whole thing off, claimed he'd stuck a pencil down his throat, but the inner cadre of fellow-travellers remained unconvinced. What if the vomiting and fainting had something to do with Sharp's repeated journeys into the knockout zone? To the great disappointment of all of us, it looked for a time as if knockouts would be permanently curtailed. The way Sharpie explained it, he was already two trips ahead of the others – no way he'd go on by himself if nobody else had the guts to keep up.

The weeks came and went and there were no takers for knockout sessions under that willow tree at the far end of the schoolyard. Sensing the rapid erosion of his power base, Dean Sharp resorted to bribery. When our crowd gathered hopefully under the willow tree on Friday afternoons he'd offer to steal the next volunteer anything he wanted from The Westside – four-inch cannon crackers? Dirty books? Hockey card gum? Name *anything* from The Westside's inventory that'd fit under a windbreaker and it was yours! The fact that no one took up this extravagant offer – not even Red Vatero, a touchy little bastard who'd done time in reform school – convinced everyone that the danger of knockouts was all too real.

It is this weave of events which surrounded Emile Hops' first day in our schoolyard and his fateful encounter with Dean Sharp under the hanging streamers of that willow tree.

Emile's Cooties

Need I confess that I didn't relish my job as Emile's official escort that first day? I was anxious enough about my own popularity without having to contend with a weird-looking geek who stuttered and stammered and showered me with spit every time he tried to say something around those amazingly crooked teeth. I knew it'd

only be a matter of time before the girls I wanted to impress started running away from me chattering about 'Emile's Cooties.' It was the kind of situation I was anxious to unload as quickly as possible. Thus, during that first Friday afternoon recess, I followed the path of least resistance and led Emile Hops directly to the willow tree where Dean Sharp stood head and shoulders above a gaggle of small fry, waiting hopefully for his buddies to arrive for another round of negotiations. After one look at Emile Hops Dean Sharp immediately began telling him all about knockouts, that glint coming to his eye as he made it sound like this was *the* most exciting part of Riverside's initiation ritual. As Sharpie winked at me and continued his pitch I thought about intervening, if only to qualify the expansive gesture he extended around the playing fields to indicate the hundreds of kids who'd given knockouts a try, and *loved* the experience so much that it was getting hard to control the lineup. Before I managed to figure out my responsibilities Emile Hops had enthusiastically agreed to undergo an immediate demonstration, honking with laughter as Sharpie described the mysterious stages of the journey which lay ahead.

Within minutes there were fifty kids bunched under the willow tree telling each other to shut up for crissakes so the teacher supervising our recess wouldn't catch wind of the commotion. As Sharp prepared to administer his chest-squeeze I found myself acting as Emile's handler, introducing him quickly around to my friends in the circle of kids, offering last-minute advice about what to expect in the next sixty seconds. Emile nodded goofily, his face slack with concentration. Then, he started taking funny shallow breaths with his eyes pinched shut as if, going under, he expected to be splashed with ice cold water. When the crowd finished its countdown Sharp squeezed mightily, a fiendish grin lighting his face. Leaning back, he lifted Emile Hops clear off the ground then tossed him aside like a sack of potatoes.

Hops was out cold with his eyes wide open!

We'd scarcely moved a step closer to check out this new phenomenon when one of the grade-eighters pushed his way into the crowd: 'Scatter! Here comes Gert!' He pointed across the playground to Mr Gerhardt, the principal, who was making for us at a furious stiff-legged trot, hollering:

'Alright! Hold it right there, Sharp! What in the name of hell – !'

'The guy fainted, sir, we – '

While Sharp tried to divert Mr Gerhardt I grabbed Emile Hops by the arm and tried to pull him to his feet. Gert gave Sharp a forearm shiver and made directly for me, jerking me around with such force that buttons popped off my shirt. I was paralyzed with fear.

'You're in Mr Carrie's class, aren't you?' he bellowed. 'What did Sharp do to him?'

'H-he's new,' I stammered. 'This is his first – '

'Enough!' Mr Gerhardt batted me aside and towered over Emile Hops, those extraordinarily lush eyebrows bunching together like wrestling caterpillars below the reddened dome of his forehead. 'And what have *you* got to say for yourself, young fellow?'

By now Emile Hops was showing signs of coming around. He wobbled to his feet and brushed at the knees of his pants, glanced around furtively.

'We was playin',' he said, indicating me with a jab of his thumb, 'I fell in a hole.'

What?

Silence. A kid in the crowd snickered, then hid it behind a cough.

Mr Gerhardt was speechless – he whapped Hops, Sharp and me on the back of the head and frog-marched us back up to the school through a gauntlet of motionless kids, down echoing corridors past grim teachers standing with their arms crossed, shoved us into his office and slammed the door with all his might. BOOM!! When Gert blew his stack the world stood still.

Mr Gerhardt claimed he knew exactly what had been going on

down there under the willow tree. He'd had a phone call that morning from Mr Kelly, the Principal over at St Agnes. Before he decided who should get the strap, or maybe even be *expelled*, he wanted our side of the story.

The slugs? Expelled? I'd never even had a detention! I started sobbing quietly. Sharp and Hops turned beet red, said nothing.

'Come along!' Gert boomed. 'Who's behind this nonsense?'

Incredibly, Emile Hops spoke up for us and, more incredible still, stuck with his story. We'd been chasing each other, he said, and he'd caught his foot in a deep hole and stubbed his big toe. Mr Gerhardt interrupted impatiently, demanded that Emile cut out the monkey business or he'd get strapped along with the rest of us, newcomer or not.

The next thing I knew, Hops was down on the floor tugging off his right sneaker, then the filthy sock, exclaiming: 'See, *there!* I told yuz!' Emile grimaced with pride as he wiggled the nail that hung like a crooked trap door from the inflamed tip of his big toe. God, what a *stink.*

You could tell from Gert's eyes that he knew he'd been had. He bent to look at Emile Hops toe skeptically, then, driven back by the stench, told him to put the sneaker back on. Before he sent us back to class Gert warned that we should now consider ourselves under permanent high-level surveillance. One way or another he'd make sure these shenanigans caught up with us.

The Hunchback

After school that day Dean Sharp treated a gang of us to free cherry cokes at The Westside, describing over and over again the way Gert had winced when Emile whipped off that filthy sock and stunk us out.

Of course, there was never to be another knockout session. Why bother? Emile Hops had brought that chapter to a fitting

conclusion – intervened to let all the main players off the hook and introduce himself into the unfolding drama. It was the fable about the horribly ugly hunchback who, by rescuing the princess, earns special status – TOENAILS! – and becomes an acceptable oddity in the village. That permanently strange stranger who is universally tolerated because he makes everybody else feel normal.

Green Novices

During those public school years a group of my chums began playing organized hockey every winter, heading off to towns with names like Hespeler and Schomberg before first light on winter mornings to square off in rough bantam and midget tournaments against big country boys who played to win. Like most bystanders I went to the odd home game and kept loose track of the top scorers, dirtiest defencemen, best goalies and the fathers who displayed the craziest devotion. I'd never played organized hockey myself. In fact I didn't even own my first pair of skates until I was ten or eleven. Inwardly, this was a bit of a problem for me. My dad had quit school to play semi-pro with the Chicago Shamrocks, one of his favourite yarns, and while he didn't in any way push me into the sport I knew he liked it when I went down to the big public rink on the Credit River to build up my ankles and work on my generally weak skating. Sometimes he'd even come along, sailing off ahead of me with those long, fluid strides, wheeling around to loiter back in lazy circles while I struggled to keep up, ankles on fire with the effort.

The September that I entered grade nine our town opened a new arena and it was announced that the local hockey ladder would immediately double in size, the expansion to include rare openings for entire teams of novices. Why not? I thought. It might be kind of fun to see what hockey was like without thirty other players milling around on a backyard rink. Besides, if everyone else on the team

was a green novice I might not look half bad in comparison.

When I told my dad I wanted to join one of the expansion clubs he went out and bought me the best equipment available – Tacklebury skates, lightweight fibreglass pads, professional quality pants and top-of-the-line leather-palmed gloves with Bobby Pulford's signature monogrammed in silver on the gauntlet. My father was never one to quibble about cost. When it came to his kids the best was hardly good enough.

My mother, meanwhile, watched all this activity from a safe and silent distance – she knew as much about hockey as she knew about ants but she understood what I was up to. She even got up at dawn to cook my breakfast the day of that first practice with the Port Credit Meteors – the novice team to which my application had been shunted. She didn't have to say anything. I knew what she was thinking. As I headed out the door I made a joke about how everybody would probably want to play goal so they could log ice time without learning how to skate and my mom laughed, pretending to understand, as she helped me hoist the duffel bag when the pick-up car honked.

Outside it was cold, dawn newly broken into that dove grey light which is the best solder for memory.

Ozzie Nelson

A moment of curious recognition. I entered the changing room full of partially-clad teammates, all nervous strangers, except for, *miraculously,* Emile Hops – TOENAILS! – who beckoned me with a loud honk of greeting, as if it'd been days rather than years since we'd last seen each other. In fact I'd totally lost track of Toenails after he quit public school halfway through grade seven and took a grim job racking duck pins at the local bowling alley, the scale of his role in my story diminishing as the surrounding boundaries expanded to include the new mystery of puberty. As Toenails talked and laughed about the happy coincidence I could tell by their silence that the other Meteors were starting to wonder about this guy in the ratty underwear.

Just then our coach walked into the dressing room – a meek looking guy in overalls who introduced himself as Mr Neilsen. He told us he'd come straight to practice after his night shift at the refinery, then introduced us to each other with a quick roll-call off his clipboard. As soon as that was done with Mr Neilsen started to talk a little bit about his expectations for this, our first practice, and the exhibition game against Moore's Smoke Shop which would follow the next week. Mr Neilsen, or Ozzie as we immediately nick-named him in honour of the TV dad, explained that this was his first year of coaching so we were all going to be learning together. Naturally, playing against the more experienced teams in our league, we shouldn't expect a winning season. The important thing was that we stick to fundamentals and learn to play as a team. For starters we had to decide who was going to wear the goalie pads – were there any volunteers? Before anyone else could even size up that opportunity Toenails was pulling one of the big leg pads out of the duffel bag. We waited for him to suit up, all of us standing now, eager for our ice time to begin, while Mr Neilsen explained about the five books of raffle tickets everyone had to sell if we wanted to keep our club in the league past Christmas. When Toenails was ready we clumped up the rubber-matted ramp and struggled out single-file into the enormous echo of the empty arena, chirping excitedly as we floundered off toward the far corners of the rink.

Now *there* was a sight.

The ice appeared to be *unbelievably* slippery. Not even the best Meteor could execute a clean turn without falling, and that included Mr Neilsen, who coasted around stiff-legged like a toy on a string. I watched from my hands and knees as Toenails came last onto the ice, huge in his goalie pads, took two running steps on his ankles and fell, picked himself up to lumber another two steps, fell again, and continued this until by the time he reached the blue line he was literally crawling toward the empty net which would be his home for the practice.

After tweeting us through a couple of incredibly clumsy drills Mr Neilsen separated out 'the bodies,' as he called us, into forward lines, composed of those who could keep a puck on their sticks while they coasted forward, and defensive pairings – the others who had trouble keeping their balance while they stood still. The resulting slow-motion scrimmage served to convince all of us that it was going to be a long, tough season.

Back in the dressing room after practice Mr Neilsen explained again about the raffle tickets and gave us each a couple of books so we could start canvassing our neighbourhoods before the team's share of the sweater bill came due. As we got ready to leave he said the only thing left to decide was who was going to play goal in our first game. The candidate had to be somebody with a ride home who could look after the huge bag of pads. Since I was the only kid with a dad waiting outside I volunteered, and was thus elevated by acclamation to the position of goaltender for our first game against Moore's Smoke Shop.

The Embers

The next afternoon my dad helped me strap on the goalie pads and put me through my paces on the driveway, slapping tennis balls from twenty feet out so I'd get used to the patterned movements of cumbersome anticipation that are a net minder's stock-in-trade. Each time the tennis ball got by me and boomed against the aluminium garage door, which was fairly often, dad would hustle in and retrieve it, bantering: 'Okay, tie game, tie game! Important shot coming up for Johnny Bower! Is he ready? Boomer's at the blue line, is Mr Bower *ready*?' then slap a dribbler straight at me so I could look good making an easy kick save.

On game day the two of us went to the plaza across from the arena and had steak sandwiches at The Embers. I was nervous, and, sensing it, my dad tried to keep me loose with little jokes about hypothetical attitudes I might adopt if we got behind three to two in the dying minutes, both of us laughing along in recognition of the fact that the road to defeat is often paved with small but significant victories which make all the difference in the long run.

It was in that spirit that we talked all the way over to the arena and downstairs into the dressing room where my father shook hands with Ozzie Neilsen, told him briefly about his own hockey background in Chicago, and left, reminding me over his shoulder to keep the blade of that stick on the ice and watch that the legs didn't drift apart when the other team was in our zone.

Inside the dressing room I took my spot on the bench beside Toenails and donned my equipment while Ozzie used the blackboard to do a 'chalk talk'. All of us Meteors were nervous. Ozzie Neilsen was so nervous his voice was shaking. Moore's Smoke was one of the best teams in the league, largely because they gave plenty of ice time to a big defenceman named Bill Tivern who had a heavy slapshot. According to Ozzie if we could hem in Bill Tivern we'd probably be able to stay close to Moore's on the scoreboard. How wonderful, I thought, to have a role in such strategy. Watching the mythology unfold in x's and arrows on a real blackboard in an authentic dressing room!

Finally the buzzer sounded and after three ragged hurrays our team clumped up the ramp to meet its uncertain fate in the echoing arena.

As usual, there was a heavy turnout of moms and dads to support Moore's. The bleachers around our end of the ice were empty except for a loitering clump of older kids waiting for our game to finish so theirs could begin. When I got to the net my dad called to me from behind the screen and gave me a double-handed wave. I tried to act preoccupied, pushing the blades of my skates side to side across the crease, evening up the ice to avoid a crazy bounce the way I'd seen the pros do it on TV. Meanwhile the rest of the Meteors coasted through their warm-up in front of my net. Most of them moved slowly, sticking close to the boards to minimize the chance of a wild fall.

Too soon, the starting line-ups faced each other at centre ice. Faint with anxiety I tried to remember the three things I was supposed to remember and watched, mesmerized, as Moore's effortlessly took the opening face-off, organized their rush with a couple of quick passes and loitered unhindered into our zone with the Meteors galloping on their ankles to keep up. The lead man dropped the puck between his legs to Bill Tivern at the blue line. Sensing our disarray, Tivern made a couple of leisurely fakes, took his time with a full backswing, then brought his stick down and through like a golfer. He connected solidly and the puck rocketed just wide of the net at waist level. KA-BOOM! The Moore's supporters rose in a blood-thirsty scream as their centre man picked up the loose puck in the corner and slapped it back to Tivern for another try. This time Tivern was waiting at the top of his backswing when the puck arrived and he let it go in one fluid motion.

I didn't even see the puck, much less have time to move. The booming shot caught me flush on the unprotected portion of my stick arm and I dropped to the ice as if shot, writhed into a tight ball, as the play went on around our net until Moore's put the puck safely behind me. By the time everyone on our team had clustered around I'd realized what was going on and done my best to stop crying. Somehow I finished that game in goal. The final score of the bizarre twenty-minute scrimmage was 19-zip – two of those goals coming when Toenails tried to turn around and skate backwards at our blue line, totally lost it, and slid headlong into the net taking me with him into the mesh.

A Hollow Ring

Back in the dressing room after that first game we Meteors were a subdued bunch, stunned by the sudden recognition of what lay ahead. My arm was still burning from Tivern's slapshot, but aside from the occasional whiffle I'd stopped crying. Even though Ozzie Neilsen tried to act calm and cheerful we could tell that he was in worse shape than the rest of us – his suggestion that it was time we elected a team captain had a particularly hollow ring. To my amazement, Toenails stood up and said he thought I should be captain because I was going to be on the ice all season filling the toughest spot in our line-up. Mr. Neilsen asked for other nominations and, after everyone had numbly shaken his head at the floor, announced that I was thereby elected Captain of the Port Credit Meteors by acclamation. He'd bring a felt 'c' for my jersey to the next practice. While I tried to smile through my lingering sniffles Toenails tore three pieces off a roll of stick tape, fashioned a crude 'c', pressed it on my left shoulder and stepped back to lead the rest of the guys in a boisterous *hip-hip-hurray*!

In that moment of public anointment Emile 'Toenails' Hops earned a special place in my memory – for I was never to be made captain of anything again, and, after I quit the team three games later, was destined to lose touch with that part of me he owned for good.

Bigger Pond

A flight of years passed high overhead, pinwheeling blades sirening across a bright spring sky. Wild irises nodded in nearby fields. A hedge, a boxwood hedge, grew wild and unattended in the backyard of a house where a Memory once had lived.

Wanton Boys

Most of us had late-model cars to drive by grade twelve and destinations we could brag about. Cruising aimlessly back and forth through town with windows down and radios up – The Hound on K.B. – all of us secure and safe in the apparent dove-tailing of our experience.

Emile Hops, meanwhile, lived out those years elsewhere, became a certified local oddity in our little village, a permanent fixture on the bridge over the Credit River in the centre of town. There he'd stand alone at all hours of the day and night, a transistor radio tinkling beside him on the rail while he fished for silver bass that he kept alive in a plastic pail at his feet. Moving from time to time to try different spots, pacing a well-trodden path back and forth across the bridge – a fixated polar bear in a public zoo. With his extravagant ducktail, studded leather jacket and heavy Wellington boots, Emile Hops had become the penultimate public example of the perdition which awaited anyone who strayed too far from the norm.

Whenever we weren't in a hurry during those Friday night rounds in our late-model wagons we'd slow down as we drove by him, hollering: 'Hey Toenails! Remember, the brown ones aren't fish!' sometimes cruising close along the curb to pelt him with half-eaten banquetburgers or, if we happened to be particularly well organized, a barrage of eggs and tomatoes. Laughing and numb as we raced away into the night. Blind in our cruelty to all the obscure, half-forgotten identities we'd left behind in the past.

The Man in the Iron Mask

Blue Irises

I was alone on the Georgian Bay island. The first visit in four summers.

A big herring gull with an eye like a gold doubloon broke crying from the rock as I approached carrying my mask, snorkel and flippers. I crossed the flat sweep of granite where the gull had been, went to the Five Boulders. The oval depression between them was full of rainwater and the clumps of wild irises were in bloom. It was perfect except that the bottoms of the catchment pools were stained bright red with some strange residue – the image at odds with the way I wanted to remember the pools of water that always filled those depressions. The five boulders, too, seemed less deliberate in their placement on the smooth open stretch of pink granite that led down to the water's edge – smaller than my childhood recollections wanted them to be. Mystery. Mystery.

I walked down to the shore, spat in my face mask to keep it from fogging, stepped out of my shorts, wet my fins and slid naked into smooth water lit amber by a low afternoon sun that was about to lose its heat.

Swimming, I followed a sloping vein of quartz away from the shore, watched the jagged light move in serrated seams across the boulder beds, re-recording all of it in my head, the exact placements I might have, but didn't, remember. Yet part of it was familiar – the laboured push of expiration through the snorkel, the gasp of breath before a duck-dive, flippering down to cross the cooler isotherm at twenty feet, mild panic as I held back against dwindling air to explore the bottom, putting weight against a dramatically

striped boulder, anything beautiful, to see if it might move or otherwise acknowledge the scale of my hand.

I popped back to the surface, blew my snorkel clear and headed away from shore, hung motionless over deeper water where gothic light found no bottom. Looking down, I saw David Phipps, my godfather, saw all of him in detail, his face projected in ethereal dimension. Heard the bizarre story that was told whenever we explained him to strangers.

The Godfather

When I knew him best David Phipps was in his mid-forties and I was twelve or thirteen, young enough to stand in awe of him, yet old enough to understand how his complex masculinity had come to assume such mythic proportions in the stories my dad told. For starters there was his war record. Phipps had applied for Officers' Candidate School at twenty and shipped out to England for basic training. After he beat the piss out of a British officer he was sentenced to 'the Glass House' for six months of sadistic discipline, then back to Canada in disgrace to face a father who had no word for failure. When the troop ship docked in Montreal David Phipps dove overboard and swam ashore, a chill October night so the story goes, and promptly re-enlisted with the paratroopers. He made his first and only combat jump on D-day, broke his back on landing, was immediately captured by the Germans and held in a P.O.W. camp until the end of the war – a survival saga purchased with contraband Hershey bars. After the war Phipps came home and went to the University of Western Ontario on the Veterans' Bill. Spent some weekends in jail. Quit in the middle of his second year. All of this is true.

For the next five years my godfather drifted and bounced through a half-dozen car-trunk-size business ventures that went nowhere. He followed the regimen of a hundred push-ups and a

MACCO

hundred sit-ups every morning to try and save the degenerating disc in his lower back. He got married and drank cooking sherry in the middle of the afternoon while he waited for his wife to come home from work to their cramped apartment on Jamieson Avenue.

Around this time David Phipps unaccountably began to hang around with my dad, his cousin, coming out to Oakville late on Sundays to have dinner with us. The two of them were closing a distance in their relationship that had opened when my father joined Alcoholics Anonymous and settled down to raise a family – my father older and wiser than his cousin – a big brother.

On those Sunday afternoons by the fire I gradually learned all the stories about David Phipps' wild and vulnerable past. Looking like Alan Ladd in his dirty sweatshirt and jeans, Phipps could make anybody laugh with his tales of stalemate and defeat in the late 50s. He didn't fit in anywhere and, because he was half in love with the romance of that condition, he was destined *never* to fit in anywhere. That's why my dad admired him so much and talked about him all the time. David Phipps was one of the men my father could have been if that bus had left the station ten minutes earlier.

Naturally enough, the two men were *very* competitive. Always daring each other to try improbable things neither could really afford. In that spirit when my dad bought an old launch to explore Georgian Bay, David Phipps simply had to follow suit, borrowing the $1,500 down-payment for the rotting hull of a cabin cruiser he'd found lying in the tall grass behind the Penetang Boat Works.

In the summers that followed we never actually saw Phipps on his boat – he docked it 200 miles further south on Georgian Bay – but that was hardly the point. It only mattered that in the winter, those fireside Sunday afternoons again, Phipps and my father were able to trade exaggerated stories about their adventures on that vast body of water which reminded them both of Lake Superior, and their childhoods. Not surprisingly, strategies for a joint expedition were finally drawn up, my father and Phipps arranging overlapping holidays in August so they could go on a two-week voyage to the top of the Bay, an expedition well beyond the charts either of them knew.

I went along on that trip with my twin brother and two of our young friends. It is halfway through that journey where the story I remembered – floating alone that afternoon off Pancake Island – began.

The Stew

Three days out and we were making good headway up the main shipping channel, the mainland a quarter-inch stubble on the horizon. Each evening we'd duck back into the archipelago of islands to strike camp, cook dinner, and sleep in tents. Each morning my father and Phipps huddled over the charts, pencilling possible routes out through the shoal-ridden jigsaw of islands to the main channel that led north to the French River.

On the fourth day of our trip the Bay kicked up and got very rough. Late afternoon found us well out in open water, still heading due north for our final destination – the Bustard Islands. The clouds had darkened oyster grey and closed the sky overhead by the time my dad and Phipps pulled their boats parallel and, rocking and pitching wildly, shouted orders at each other – we should head straight in and seek anchorage in the lee of the first set of reefs. My father's boat led with Phipps and me following. Dark water and grey sky merged in the failing light. Phipps sat on top of his cruiser's cabin with his legs dangling through a hole he'd chopped in the roof so he could steer with his feet. Down below I held on, trembling with chill anxiety, my body lost in the folds of Phipps' duffel coat, his dog Shaddrach moaning and whimpering at my feet.

At the bottom of each trough the wind whipped back a sheet of ice water that caught Phipps flush on the chest, the water running in rivers down his legs into the cabin. His toes held the spokes of the wheel steady, then spun it as the boat skewed sideways and lost direction in the following sea. All the while Phipps sang in a tuneless tenor, pausing only to shake off the cold spray that drenched him at the bottom of each swell, sang: 'Me and my shadow / All alone as we can be,' just those two lines, over and over again.

In the last hour before sunset the water grew shallow, cobalt suddenly light blue, and my father slowed his boat to a crawl to pick his way through the treacherous waters that led to barren reefs in the distance. Phipps jockeyed his boat to within a dozen yards of my father's stern while the relentless following sea crested and broke around us. It was clear that this was a route to anchorage neither man would have chosen had the other not been present. As usual, they were trying to out-crazy each other.

As the boats wallowed in toward protected anchorage enormous boulders broke the surface right alongside us. I was petrified! Up on the roof Phipps had stopped singing 'Me & My Shadow,' he was shouting at my father now, trying to get his attention, his voice lost to the wind. Suddenly, a hundred yards out from the whaleback reefs, Phipps pulled the throttle wide open with the toes of his left foot and we shot toward the transom of my father's boat, missed it by inches as Phipps spun the wheel with his right foot – pulled parallel, then ahead, careening through a narrow gap between the shoals – a miraculous moment later we were in calm water on the leeside of the reef. The whole manoeuvre took maybe ten seconds. David Phipps throttled back with the toes of his left foot and pulled the boat out of gear with his right. He was laughing like a madman coughing and wheezing when it got too, *too* funny. He stuck his head down through the hole in the roof, his upside-down face broken with a crazy grin.

'Watch your old man!' Phipps said, 'He'll come coasting through there in neutral with two guys on the bow holding him off the rocks with a pike pole.'

'Yeah!' I said. 'That was *neat*!'

As predicted, my dad crept between the reefs with two guys on the bow, then turned his boat in to shore and went about the business of docking without paying any attention to Phipps. As soon as my twin brother and his friends had scrambled up the steep rock face with his bowline, my dad walked back to the stern and waited for Phipps to move in close and toss a bowline to snub on the transom cleat, the boats then secured into the prevailing wind by splayed stern anchors Phipps would set in the deep water off his own stern. As Phipps manouevred his boat into position my dad offered advice with a calm voice, suggesting that that was okay and Phipps should cut his engine, suggesting more strongly that Phipps had better cut his – then shouting: 'Reverse! *Reverse*!' My godfather's cruiser coasted straight in, too fast to deflect, and hammered the transom of my father's boat so solidly that dad was knocked off his feet. *You stupid fuck*!

In or Out

By the time the two men, hostile and silent now, established the proper balance between shore lines and anchor lines, black storm clouds had enclosed the entire sky. In a race with the rising storm we chained our cooking gear up onto the crest of the rock and down onto the other, the windy side, to the place where we would reheat the previous evening's stew by the wild, breaking waves. We kids chose a spot high on the crest of the rock to huddle under our unzipped sleeping bags while Phipps and my dad lit the stoves and sullenly shared their first cup of fresh coffee since morning. When they began to speak again, my dad tried to lighten things up but Phipps kept pushing, needling him about the way my old man had chosen to navigate that final gap and what it might have meant if the Bay had been *really* rough, bad in the way that Phipps had seen

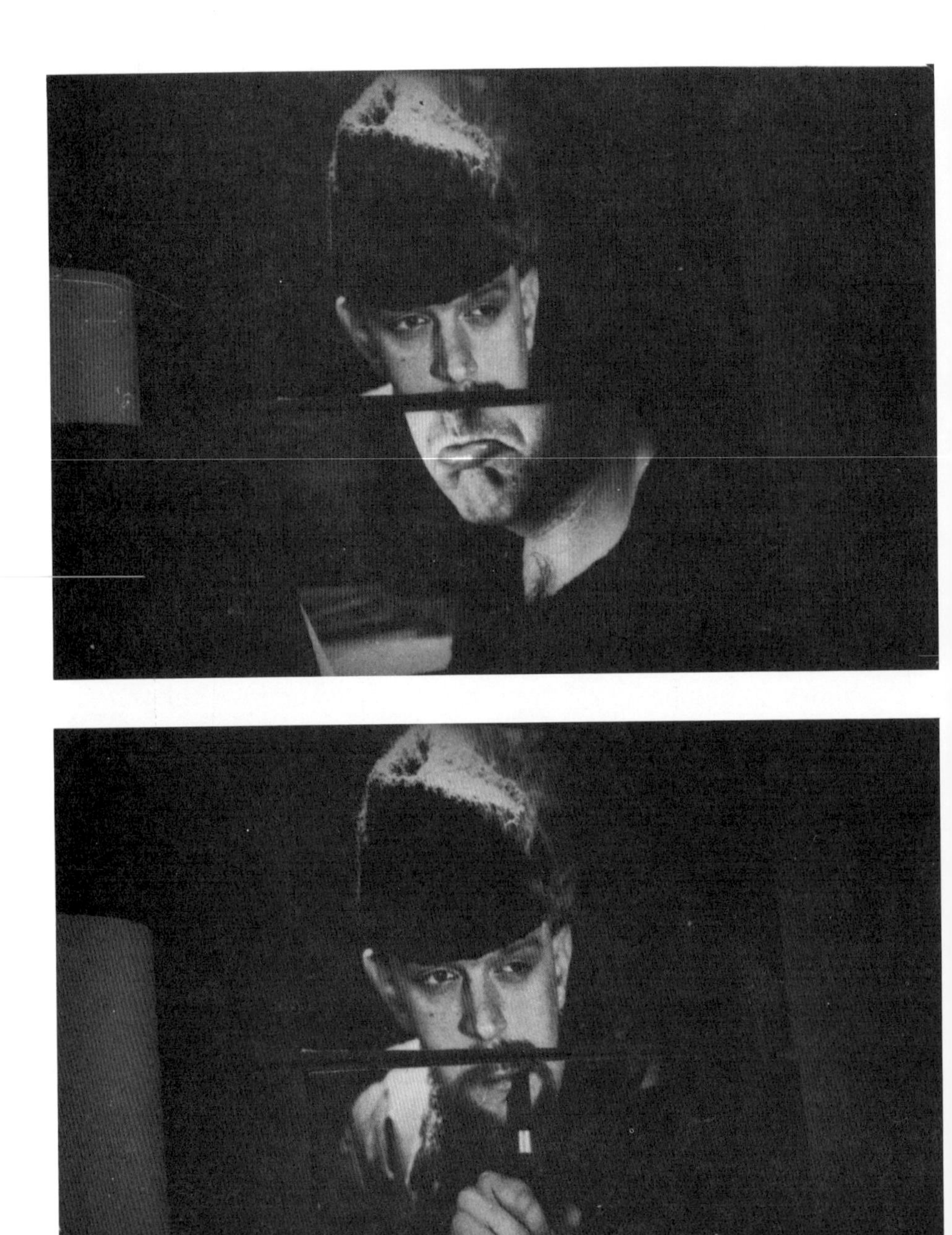

it during solo trips in November when the water was so damn cold you didn't want your hand in it.

At sunset the low unbroken ceiling of cloud split open an inch at the horizon and a section of sun, red and grotesquely fat with atmospheric distortion, grew to fill the narrow slit.

Phipps paced around the fire drinking deep from a bottle of whisky. He was the kind of alcoholic who never got entirely drunk or entirely sober.

Putting down the bottle of whisky Phipps said: 'It's time Shad and I had our swim.' Without waiting for a response he dropped his shorts, put on the jockstrap he always wore in the water and went straight down to the place where the waves came up black from the deep and thundered on the rocks.

My father followed a few steps behind, an irritated voice: 'C'mon Phipps, don't be so goddamn crazy! Dinner's almost ready – that water's not for swimming.'

Phipps pretended he didn't hear that, sucked on his whisky bottle, put it down on the rock and said to no one in particular: 'Who the fuck is *that* guy?' then dove straight off into the boiling retreat of a breaker, took a couple of strokes and turned, treading water while he coaxed Shaddrach in after him. Then, with powerful even strokes he headed straight out – slapping the water right arm, slapping the water left arm, head up for a slow breath, slapping the water right arm, slapping the water left arm, head up for another breath, the dog half out of the water in his eager attempt to keep up as they swam away from the reef toward the place where the sun was disappearing.

A chill edge came into the wind. In a half-hour it'd be pitch black. My father slopped hot stew into our plastic bowls and sat up on the rock with us. For the next fifteen minutes we ate quietly and watched while my godfather swam straight out toward the darkening horizon, not stopping to tread water until his head and the dog's head had merged in a single bobbing dot that periodically

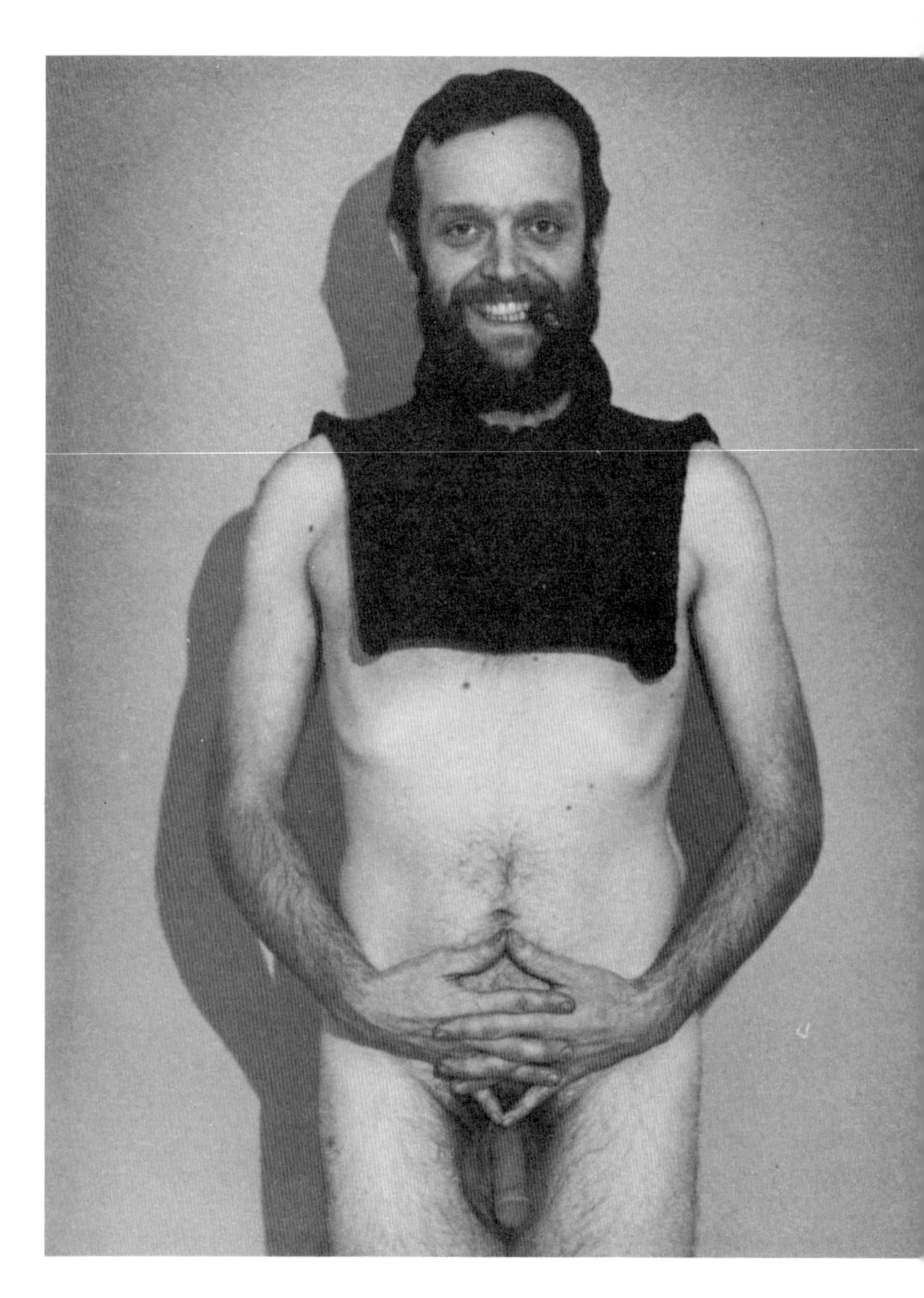

appeared and disappeared in the huge waves. After we'd finished eating and stacked our dirty bowls by the fire my dad smoked a cigarette and told derisive little anecdotes about other men he'd known who thought they were tough, doing his best to mask an unspoken concern that was too real for all of us.

It was nearly dark when Phipps came back in, floundering a little in the pounding sea before he managed to crawl up the rock on all fours through the suck-back of retreating waves, gasping for breath as he came to his feet. He pulled his exhausted dog out of the water, then stripped off his jockstrap and swaggered naked and triumphant up the rock into the light of our fire. He knew himself to be miraculously handsome. We kids watched him from behind the fortress of sleeping bags we'd built against the wind. My dad sat off to one side, sipping coffee.

'I see it's still there,' he snorted.

Phipps flipped the shrivelled stub of his pecker with a self-conscious grimace, 'And another Musky goes to bed hungry. Don't suppose you clowns remembered to leave chow for me and Shad – '

'In the pot.'

Phipps, acting as if he was utterly alone in the world, paraded naked and untowelled around the fire, picked up a bowl for his dog from the stack of dirty dishes, filled it with stew from the pot on the Coleman stove and slapped it down on the rock. No darkness, no cold wind, no speechless audience – just the end of another normal day for David Phipps. He watched while the exhausted Lab finished the bowl of stew in a couple of swallows, then picked up the empty dish and used his wet jock strap to swab it out, put the jockstrap back on, re-filled the dish with stew and, squatting by the fire, ate chunks of meat and potato with his bare hands. Not quite as quick as the dog, but more noise.

Later that night David Phipps sat on the back seat in my dad's boat and polished off a bottle of Spanish brandy. Trading stories with my old man about the Northern Ontario bush where they'd

both grown up and the bizarre escapades of blood relatives and fellow travellers who stayed behind up there to hold the past, all of them half-crazy to either get out, or further in, once and for all.

Days, Weeks & Months

The following summer my family skipped Georgian Bay in favour of a car trip to Nova Scotia, all except for my brother who stayed behind with his first summer job and the breathless luxury of my mom's station wagon and a house with full liquor cabinets. In late August we returned home – my parents, my sister and I – arriving exhausted after an eighteen-hour drive from the ferry at Trois Rivières.

My brother waited half an hour before he broke the news.

Late in July David Phipps had left Toronto on a Friday afternoon, just he and Shaddrach. They'd driven up to his boat in Midland. In the middle of the next week his boat had come ashore carrying an empty whisky bottle and a note that mysteriously disappeared (his wife's doing thanks to a sympathetic nod from the local cops). A few days later a commercial fisherman found Phipps floating face-up in the open Bay off Penetang – a bloated decoy, eyes taken by the gulls. They never found the dog.

Hearing this, my father sagged toward a chair, missed his mark sitting down, fell to his knees on the rug, and wept. A loud chaotic noise that made all of us nervous. It was the first and last time I was ever to see him cry.

It went on for weeks. The lawn grew long and tangled, turned into an unkempt field. After dinner my father wandered around in circles out there, came in after nightfall and made hushed long-distance calls to relatives in the Lakehead who knew enough about Phipps to understand.

The blue irises that grew thick along the back wall of our garden bloomed and withered before my mother found the time to cut the flowers and bring them indoors. My pals at school respected me in a new way because my godfather had had the guts to kill himself.

In Tempo

Haunted waters below, nearly dark now that the sun had lost its final penetration, its last afternoon warmth. I hung motionless, vertical in the still water, and studied the rasp and return of my breath through the snorkel, the rhythm strangely mild and untroubled by my slow flutterkick away from that island that was my childhood. Me, a floating caricature on location in the past, the unchanging world of Nature watching from the distance as I tried to explain away the enduring failure of mind over matter in the male psyche. All of it complete and utter bullshit. Complete and utter bullshit. I kicked up and checked my shore bearings through the face plate, a hundred yards at most, far closer than I'd imagined. I turned and headed in, kicking hard and using my arms now, rehearsing the lyrics of a half-forgotten song in tempo with the steady exertion, certain, for the time being at least, that no verse could ever be left behind.

Lacuna

CONVERGENCE

Rusty Taps

An American in Paris

I don't know when exactly it was that the idea of dancing began to fascinate me. It may well have originated with Mr Cluff, the ballroom instructor who held classes on alternate Friday evenings at Riverside public school during the winter term – although, in retrospect, there was something so Soviet about the way Mr Cluff separated boys from girls on opposite sides of the gym, made us face each other across a no-man's-land and zombie through box-step exercises for half the evening before we got to 'mix.' More certainly my consuming avidity for the momentum and grace of what those dancers were doing 'out there' came with my first exposure to Gene Kelly at the Vogue Theatre in September of 1957.

I'd gone to the movie with my mother – a rare cultural event in itself – and to this day have vivid recall of Kelly, muscular in a striped T-shirt, alternately euphoric and downcast as he leapt from pillar to crag on a set bathed in sapphire blue light, the chorus crooning:

The song of love is a sad song
Hi-lily, Hi-lily, Hi-lo

There was something so masculine and *vulnerable* in the tough yet tender texture of Kelly's quick movements and abrupt, absorbed, hesitations which would come to characterize my own fantasies about male sexuality in the years to come.

Slurping

On a sultry evening in July of 1970 I found myself in Madrid having dinner at El Hogar Gallego, an expensively quaint seafood house on Plaza Mayor that enjoyed a four-spoon rating in the *Guide Rouge*. My companions that evening were two lovely young American girls – Iris White, a textile heiress from New England, and Sarah Duke, whose father oversaw the strip-mining of substantial bauxite properties in Jamaica. Halfway through our *calamares* a man and woman took the table next to ours. The man was a vulgar, loud-mouthed American who'd evidently had too much to drink and, judging from the brackish colour of his skin, spent an unhealthy period of time exposed to the roasting sun of the Costa Brava. His female companion, many years younger, was Spanish, coarse of complexion yet fashionably attired, the kind of woman who inspired young Spaniards in the square to say: *Crescio alimentando los cerdos y alora la alimentan* – she grew up feeding the pigs and now they feed her.

During the pauses in the conversation at our table I eavesdropped on theirs. The American was, indeed, well into his cups, but between slurping mouthfuls of *gazpacho* he made it clear to the young woman that, despite his drunkenness, the pleasures of their evening were far, far from over.

I suppose our dinner was nearly complete, perhaps we were lingering over brandy, when I at last focused my attention on the features of that man who'd been sitting so close to me all evening and realized, beyond any doubt, that I was in the presence of Gene Kelly. Granted, the crisp geometry of his jaw line had degenerated into slack folds or, as the English have it, 'obtained character,' but once I'd focused on the young features inside the old face I made the connection. The smoky rasp of his voice doubly confirmed my conviction, the lilting syncopation was *there*! This was Gene Kelly

from the Vogue Theatre in Port Credit, alive and well in Madrid in 1970 – *Hi-lily, Hi-lily, Hi-lo!*

As their table argued about desserts and liqueurs I excitedly whispered this discovery to my companions. Being ten years my junior, neither of them had any clear sense of who Gene Kelly was, but, as I quickly placed him alongside Astaire, who still lived and danced on specials, their wonder specials, their wonder I resisted. Although undoubtedly Gene Kelly, this man was also very drunk and becoming increasingly boorish with his young lady friend. Since my companions insisted, offering small wagers in their enthusiasm, I pushed back my chair and, timing being what it was, followed Kelly as he lumbered away from his table toward the men's room.

When I entered the lavatory, Gene Kelly was already at the stalls, looking up toward the place where the wall joined the ceiling as he relieved himself.

I took a place one position removed from him and waited for his eyes to leave their study of the antique timbers and notice me.

They did not.

Finally I said, joining his eyes at the ceiling: 'You're Gene Kelly, aren't you?'

His eyes slid slowly down the wall, as if tracking a drool of paint. He turned his attention to me. Ice blue eyes.

'What of it?'

'I like your movies,' I said enthusiastically, smiling and nodding.

'Movies?' he slurred, 'Yeah, I made a couple movies. *What of it?*'

I thought for a moment. He looked around my face like a doctor examining a skin condition. We were zipping up.

'What are you up to these days?' I said, finally.

'I'm trying t'get laid. What are you up to these days?'

Before I could respond Gene Kelly pushed away from the urinal, removing his liverish eyes from me for good as he lurched toward the door, muttering 'Later, alligator.'

By the time I arrived back at my table Gene Kelly was halfway across the room, barging through the crowd with his young escort in tow. She struggled to free her wrist but he was far too strong and the entire restaurant turned to watch their noisy exit. We could hear them yelling at each other right out into the street.

When Iris White and Sarah Duke coaxed me for details about what had gone on back there in the men's room I played it cool and straight, allowed as how Gene and I had had a very genial chat. Gene had suggested that it might be good fun if I called him at his hotel the next day so we could meet for a drink someplace. Unfortunately, that was out of the question since the three of us were catching a train for Ibiza first thing the next morning.

'Isn't that always the way?' I said.

The young women nodded and listened while I changed the subject. Their faces – cocooned in the silk of this memory – are clearly astonished by my utter lack of disappointment.

Mondo Pocono

Lester Pearson & Lucky Luciano

The Poconos. *The Poconos.* Who among us can whisper those magic words without visualizing cheek-to-cheek newlyweds up to their chins in bubblebath, a magnum of domestic champagne on the edge of their Jacuzzi? And who could put aside that glossy four-colour brochure without imagining what those same honeymooners – their private areas chafed and sore – had been doing to each other on the giant circular bed in the adjoining room. If you're one of those folks who've always been a bit curious about The Poconos then this is your lucky day. While I don't know *all* the answers, I can at least get you headed in the right direction.

First question: Exactly what are The Poconos? A: Contrary to popular belief The Poconos are not 'mountains in Pennsylvania.' Rather, The Poconos are reclaimed tailings from high grade anthracite deposits extracted from that region in the late 19th century.

Second question: How did The Poconos come to be synonymous with the whole concept of 'the integrated honeymoon domain'? A: Largely because of an elderly gentleman named Earl Lumb who, since 1946, has been the sole proprietor of Lumb's-in-the-Poconos – 'a garden estate dedicated to sumptuous luxury, a full range of supervised activities. And total privacy,' as his eight-page, full-colour brochure has it. The fact is, Earl Lumb single-handedly *invented* the concept of newlyweds sitting up to their chins in the scented foam of a fully-mirrored Jacuzzi. It was his salesmanship which lent respectability to luxurious accommodation designed

specifically for the sexual congress of virgins.

In the last twenty years the vinyl/veneer motifs of Lumb's Greco-Roman decor have been slavishly imitated by his many competitors along the reclaimed ridges that surround Cresco (pop. 1700) but the other newlywed resorts are still light years behind. There is only one honeymoon hideaway in the world that can claim to have one hundred indoor swimming pools. And Earl Lumb intends to keep it that way. He was fond of reminding us the tide turned for his operation in the spring of '59 when *Look Magazine* did a photo essay on the pleasures of postwar brides which featured prominent mention of Lumb's spa, noting along the way that one weekend he'd played host to the newlywed daughters of Lester Pearson and Lucky Luciano.

The Velvet Cushion

In June of 1967 I left Toronto to work at Lumb's-in-the-Poconos. I went after the job because it was the first opening for portrait photography I'd found in the Toronto paper and I was eager to repay the two thousand bucks I'd borrowed to outfit myself as a freelancer. Concurrently, I was in chaotic retreat from the smouldering ruin of my first serious relationship. I had to put as much physical space as possible between myself and that dreadfully revealing disaster. In the process of maturing, the girl I'd fallen in love with as a freshman had abrogated all our idealistic vows about integrity to pursue a career in the brokerage business. Left me alone at home to polish that nugget of existential kaka I'd mounted on a velvet cushion in the centre of my life.

And so it was that I answered that newspaper advertisement and boarded a Greyhound bus headed for Pennsylvania. I'd never taken a portrait in my life.

Elderly Greeks

I arrived in Cresco late in the afternoon and was greeted by Earl Lumb Jr. He pumped my hand as I got off the bus, said he'd memorized my face from the application photograph I'd sent his dad. Earl Jr. certainly knew how to keep the old ball rolling! Used words the way a hummingbird uses flowers as we drove out to his dad's honeymoon resort.

When we got to the main gate Earl Jr. slowed to a crawl 'Carrera marble. Top to bottom. Do you read me?'

The next thing I knew baby Earl was walking me across more marble in the front lobby. We went straight into his father's private office.

Earl Lumb Sr. looked exactly like his son, only slightly melted. A deeply lined face, hair dyed jet black – weirdly robust, like one of those elderly Greeks who can dance all night with a chair in his teeth.

Earl Sr. pumped my hand and mussed my hair. Boy, was he glad to see *me*! He waited until his son had left the room, then smiled cagily.

'What do you think of the boy?'

'Liked him a whole bunch,' I said, 'we hit it off right away!'

Earl Lumb smiled too. 'That's real good t'hear. Your portraits, right?'

'You betcha!' I said. I started to unzip my portfolio case but Earl Lumb dismissed that idea with a wave of his hand and, sitting me down, began talking real fast.

As of that moment I was in charge of the Bridlepath Portrait Salon. Totally responsible for the whole shebang. The last guy went sick in the head. Slipped away in the middle of the night! Middle of the bloody high season too! Stinkin' kraut. Probably a queer. Earl Lumb leaned across his desk, smiled like an undertaker:

'Ain't that *always* the way?'

I'd clear $75 a week plus a percentage of the gross I generated during the five-day/six-night packages Earl retailed for six-ninety-nine. To get the volume rolling right away Earl encouraged me to utilize what he called 'user-seller momentum,' which meant that at the start of every package I should go all out for a Day-One sale so that the resulting bridal suite portfolio could be displayed during the Luau that we featured on Day Two. Seeing a sample portfolio hot off the press would get the other brides excited and they'd start nagging Charlie for memento albums of their own.

The First Sunday Afternoon

With this running start in mind I tried to get my hustle off the ground as soon as the charter buses rolled in with their loads of junketing newlyweds on that first Sunday afternoon. Our staff strategy during the frantically busy check-in was to make certain that everyone tossed back at least two snifters of Lumb's Love Potion – a mind-snapping punch of vodka, domestic champagne and cherry brandy – and then, as Earl Lumb liked to say with a wry wink, 'Get 'em into the breeding barns before they have a chance to feel shy.' The officer in charge of this critically important operation was 'Honest Phil,' our frenetic social director who'd been at Lumb's for over 20 years.

On that first Sunday afternoon Honest Phil stood barefoot on the deep, wine-coloured shag inside the main door wearing the white dinner jacket, the purple Bermuda shorts and the Day-Glo orange hunting cap which were his trademark. 'Hey, I'm Honest Phil!' Funny. Filthy! Shaking hands and chatting up each new couple like he was some long lost wise guy from high school chemistry. And Honest Phil was *good*! Babbling this filthy Shecky Green spiel and acting so totally wacked out that right away the newlyweds had something harmless and zany to compare notes about while they waited among strange companions for the Love Potions to take effect.

Meanwhile, I circulated in my Bill Blass Foreign Legion outfit distributing full-colour brochures. If anybody asked I plugged the most expensive photo grouping we offered –

'OVER THE THRESHOLD,
UNDER THE SHEETS,
IN THE BUBBLES
AND
ON THE MEMORY CHAIR'

a full colour 8 x 10 portfolio mounted in monogrammed naugahyde. All for $99.00 (plus federal and state taxes and gratuity).

During my first Sunday afternoon in the lobby it took a while to gauge how close I should stay to the amoebic periphery of Honest Phil's jabbering passage through the crowd. Too close, they were freaked. Too far away, they were frozen. Everyone said the initial pitch was by far the toughest and most important. All the newlyweds would be jittery with a stash of travellers' cheques that had to last out the week – and they hadn't even seen their semi-detached chalets yet! – much less figured out how best to dispense their 'mad money' on those tempting extras they'd seen in the brochure. Pedicures? Fly Fishing Lessons? Glass blowing? Geisha massage? Hot Lava Baths? There was no way of telling how adventurous – how sensuous and *naughty* – they might feel on the tail-end of a six-day/five-night bender at Lumb's.

Tartan Bellbottoms

Before I explain how I met Ted and Sarah Duke during one of those Sunday afternoon receptions in the main lobby at Lumb's-in-the-Poconos I should remind you that all this was taking place in 1967 – if only because that fact has no bearing on the appearance of the lobby full of young newlyweds we here imagine. Needless to say, those who found their way to Lumb's-in-the-Poconos in 1967 weren't the kind who characteristically put hard questions to society. These shiny-faced kids bore no resemblance to those belligerent minorities who were making heard their noisy demands in other sectors of North America. On the contrary, these youngsters were wholeheartedly of their parents' generation. The kind of candy-eyed kids who saw nothing irregular about striped seersucker over tartan. Or Art Linkletter. Or the joint savings account which made a fifteen-hundred-dollar honeymoon affordable once it was all 'legal.' I found their single-minded insistence on propriety strangely compelling. It was clear that in the year 2000 Earl Lumb's customers would be teaching their grandchildren the fundamentals of decency and fair play no matter what happened out there in the gritty sprawl of the world. There was bed rock certainty in that, a promise of well-being warm and secure as grammy's Johnny Cake.

What then of Ted and Sarah Duke from Tillsonburg, Ontario – what sets them apart as the couple that radiates from the centre of this remembrance of mindless conformity? It is difficult to say, except through description.

Description

Ted Duke was about fifty, and sort of arty-looking – the salt and pepper hair smoothed back over his ears, his faded denims in relaxed counterpoint to an elegant linen blazer worn over a pearl silk shirt. Around his throat Ted wore a tangle of gold chains from which hung a coptic cross, a shark's tooth and the inevitable crab of cancer. In his own way, Ted Duke was an 'up-market' kind of guy. The only thing clearly discernible in the sag of his face was that this fella obviously liked to take his first martini early in the afternoon. The kind of guy who was paying for something bad that had happened years before. You could smell the stink of failure on him.

Ted Duke took the brochure I offered in the lobby that Sunday afternoon and scanned it with the slow intensity of a small-town businessman, which he was. (I found out later he manufactured curling rocks.) He tried to ask intelligent questions as he followed the tip of his finger under the sentences, like: What's this here about a 'morning-after portrait in the Memory Chair'?

Our Memory Chair is an exact replica of a Shaker-built rocker, I replied, something you'll only find at Lumb's-in-the-Poconos. Built to scale – only *ten times* life size! That's a full size step-ladder right there beside it in the brochure – see? If you and Mrs Duke climb up on our Memory Chair it'll make for one heckuva picture. Look good in the den ten years from now. Never stops being unique until you and the little women are both senile!

Uh-huh, he said, smiling limply, uncapping his fountain pen to sign up for my most expensive package with the bold diagonals of a George Knudson. If this man didn't know what he wanted he at least knew what *somebody* wanted. Smiling, I directed my attention to the young woman behind him, the new Mrs Duke I presumed. I started to introduce myself, then stopped as she cocked her head a little and eagerly returned my attention – a kind of blank intensity in her eyes.

Sarah Duke could have been in her late teens, easily young enough to be Ted's daughter. She was dressed like a cartoon Indian mixed dutch-doors style with a brownie caught at the ripest moment of puberty – braids held back from a centre part with a woven headband, a fringed buckskin jacket, its flowered breastplate zipped open to reveal a Girl Guide's tunic which, after stretching tight to accommodate a full bosom, fell straight to her knobby knees. Bermuda socks and a scuffed pair of Buster Browns finished off the look. The fashion trends weren't going to catch up with this little enchilada for a a good ten years.

I blinked at her, felt as if we'd seen each other before – must have shown that in my face. She lifted an eyebrow, a small smile.

'Pictures?' she said, extending a hand, her eyes teasing with some secret, 'My name is Sarah.'

If this wasn't a true story I'd swear a blue spark arced between our palms.

Short Sequence

Here could follow a long sequence – the fugitive couple getting acquainted socked foot to socked foot under a banquet table at the Luau. That first secret kiss under the arbour of plastic grapes that led to The Little Girl's Room, Sarah murmuring: 'But I want to know how you *feel.* Inside me, I mean.' Then a lush description of our first four a.m. rendezvous in the hollow of a pitch'n'putt sand trap. The two of us writhing wildly out of our clothes – our coupling urgent, rich with new and exotic smells.

Predictably, all of this must culminate on the final night of our package when Ted Duke unexpectedly crawls back from the cocktail lounge to find Sarah and me joyously panting and slapping our wet bellies together in his cedar scented sauna. Ted withdraws instantly, grinning like an idiot – clicks the glass door shut and begins a vodkaesque soliloquy that's so embarrassing Sarah and I pretend we can't hear it. A moment later we emerge in terrycloth robes and Ted starts to hiccup uncontrollably. When Sarah steps forward to help Ted's face suddenly twists into a wolverine snarl and he ducks behind his fists, then starts to giggle, wobbling unsteadily toward her with a goggle-eyed smirk. I tug Sarah back by the sleeve.

'M'ye piss, Miss?'

He parrots the phrase over and over again until it sounds like an Anglo Saxon curse. An instant later he loses his balance, falls face first, catches the edge of the dresser at the last possible moment.

'Watch the television!' Sarah shrieks.

'YOU WATCH THE FUCKING TELEVISION!' Ted snatches a twenty-dollar bill off the top of it, whirls around and heads for the door, stops with his left foot planted dead centre on a half-eaten club sandwich – turns to glare at Sarah.

'I can learn from this, okay?' He straightens his tie. 'See you kids at breakfast.'

Gone.

A moment later Sarah is weeping. I try to make her laugh but it doesn't work. A few minutes after that I'm at the window, wet-eyed, Sarah watching in silence. More time passes. We're lying side by side on the shag rug. The sky grows grey and everything is ridiculous. Glorious. The clock radio clicks on – an early bird DJ who calls himself 'the morning mayor' is rhapsodizing about Charlie Pride as if the guy discovered penicillin. We try not to listen but it's impossible. We look at each other and start to laugh uncontrollably.

'You're nuts!'

'Look who's talking.'

We scribble our addresses on a table napkin and tear it in half. Then we're standing yards apart in the hall listening to the clunkety-clunk of the ice machine. Sarah is half in and half out of her door, staring at my feet as I back away down the hall. Both of us know it's over ... if only ... if only.

'Am I a memory yet?'

'Jesus – '

'Just gimme a straight answer, okay? Am I a memory, or not?'

Sarah smiles and shakes her head as she brings the door to: 'I'll think about it.'

But we must go beyond this physical description, frame it with psychological insight. Theories that explain why Sarah and I continued to correspond and telephone each other in the middle of the night months after she'd returned to the solid reality of Tillsonburg with her new husband. The way each of us had tried to prepare for the jump – that Sunday morning reunion at the train station. The things we were thinking while we searched for each other in the crowd. The way we planned out a future together, kicking autumn leaves in High Park. That first apartment. Then, six months later, our first serious argument. The make or break decision to rent a whole house on our first anniversary. The way we lost track of the fights during the troubled second year. That first physical violence manifest on the third anniversary of our enraptured sand trap episode – our remembrances of the original premise differing after a bottle of cheap Spanish brandy, our versions of the romance shorter and open to more brittle interpretation than we'd cared to imagine in the days when everything seemed possible.

Goodbye

Sarah had been fired from her third waitressing job in six months, I was slugging it out in Canada's leading portrait factory, going to work early and coming home late so Sarah would have the time she insisted she needed to get in touch with her personal space. I claimed that I was the only one in the world who'd ever understood her. Deep inside she was actually a little girl playing make-believe with her mom's high heels. Of course, I knew this was a grossly distorted half-truth, but used it anyway because it got such a solid rise out of her. You should have heard the stuff she was saying about me.

Like all lovers nearing the end we were full of accusations. Neither of us wanted to take responsibility for the habits that held our safe but boring anchorage, the patterns that no longer connected us to the people we had become. The attacks and counter attacks were hideously thorough, we knew everything about each other and nothing was out of bounds. Periodically these psychological slug-fests culminated in brief episodes of real physical violence which, if the pain threshold was properly situated, connected us in turn to the last vestiges of our sexuality. We'd fuck like scorpions,

SPECIAL
THIS MONTH
GLOVES

the pain we generated in each other flowing down to a darkly exhilarating climax. I think the medical term is Gallows Coitus. Of course this pleasure at the end of our worst arguments was never openly discussed. A label would have spoiled it, this the last of our tacit agreements.

So while I, in shop parlance, 'froze faces' for fourteen hours a day, Sarah puttered around the house in her kimono, drinking pot after pot of ginseng tea until her French cigarettes had built limpid shoals of smoke in the late afternoon light. My world was dry and hopelessly compromised, she said. It was essential that she act independently before her choice of possible commitments dwindled even further.

By late autumn Sarah and I knew we weren't going to last out the winter, groused playfully about the upcoming challenge of moving our ponderous, second-hand furniture in the semi-twilight of some February afternoon, these exchanges only possible when our shattered love-making had left us exhausted and tender in the empty sorrow we felt for each other and the strangers we'd become.

'I wonder where I'll be in five years?' Sarah would whisper, spooning closer to me.

'Looking back at this shit and asking questions,' I'd reply, 'Just like the rest of us.'

Her groan: 'Will that be all Mr Beckett?' then a pinch on the ass, giggles, sighs, Sarah snuggling into me like the little girl she knew I needed as we drifted skin to skin into the jagged terrain of dreams we'd recount with half-asleep voices when my alarm clock sounded at dawn the next morning.

The Ukrainian Kid

On the last day it snowed for hours and I trudged home earlier than usual, a daring surprise, with a good bottle of Bordeaux and a steak in my shoulder bag. Our house was dark except for a light in the upstairs sunroom where Sarah kept her bed. I let myself in and kicked off my boots in the vestibule, sensing again the way she kept my section of the house dark and cold when I wasn't home.

Halfway up the stairs a floorboard groaned in the darkened hallway. Whispers, then her giggle. A man's voice – SHHHHHH!

I stopped, one hand on the bannister.

The light at the top of the stairs clicked on. Sarah stood there with the son of our Ukrainian landlord – an arrogantly dim-witted young buck who washed and waxed his custom-painted Corvette in the driveway every Saturday – Meatloaf booming on the eight-track. The Ukrainian kid and I had never tried to hide our mutual dislike for one another. He eyed me steadily from the top of the stairs – shoved the damp hair back off his forehead and tucked in his shirt – daring me to do anything but let him pass as he started down with Sarah a step behind. The buttons of Sarah's kimono were undone and she held the front closed with one hand. I didn't move or say a word as they passed me on the stairs. Perhaps I reddened slightly as I felt the Ukrainian kid's expression twist as he eyed me and bent to pull on his cowboy boots in the vestibule, murmuring to Sarah about some movie he'd decided they should see the following afternoon. Sarah's responses were slightly giddy. She helped the Ukrainian kid put on his coat and made a show of tying his scarf for him, as if it didn't matter in the least that I watched from half-way up the stairs because this was part of a new life she was occupying through some agreed-upon entitlement. I felt my rage gathering toward a super-cold pinprick, the way only Sarah could focus it. When her lips touched his in a modest farewell buss I said: 'You'd best go with him, Sarah – I might do you some harm if you stay.'

Sarah whirled around to face me, eyes flashing, her voice shrill, the sing-song of a little girl proud to be cruel:

'Who do you think you are, Charles Bronson?' She yanked my

windbreaker off the wall hook and pulled it on over her kimono, glared at me defiantly as the Ukrainian kid held the front door open for her.

'Sarah,' I cautioned, moving down a step toward them, 'I hope you know what you're doing – '

'I don't know anything, remember?' she hissed, stepping out into the darkness. She slammed the door behind her with both hands.

There was snow on the ground and she wasn't even wearing shoes.

Acting on instinct I bounded to the bottom of the stairs, fumbled around until I found Sarah's favourite calfskin boots and trotted outside with them. As I loped across the front lawn the Corvette's headlights popped on, the engine turned over a couple of times, coughed, and roared fiercely into life. When I rapped my knuckle on the passenger window and held up Sarah's boots the Ukrainian kid shot his hand across and punched down her door lock. Sarah kept her eyes straight ahead out the windshield. She didn't even blink when I slammed her boots against the fender.

The Corvette came into gear and rolled slowly ahead. I trotted alongside the car as the Ukrainian kid pulled it across the centre of the street in a slow U-turn, dashed ahead to block the road in front of him. The Ukrainian kid coasted the Corvette straight toward me at about ten miles an hour. He wasn't going to stop. The instant before impact I jumped onto the car's sloping hood, still holding Sarah's favourite boots in one hand, and held on as the Ukrainian kid accelerated quickly down the street, thundering back into low gear at the first stop sign, hammering the brakes to try and shake me off. I spat on the windshield in front of the Ukrainian kid's face and pounded the roof of the car with the calfskin boots, momentarily floundering with loss of balance as the Vette's custom slicks peeled on the pavement, rocketing us around the corner and down the street toward the brightly lit shopping district that stretched along Bloor.

The bellicose thunder of the Corvette's straight pipes was enough to make everyone in the street turn and watch us go by. The placid yet eager excitement in Sarah's face was indescribable. She lit a cigarette with fumbling fingers and watched me flounder to stay aboard as the Ukrainian kid de-accelerated for the first red light.

'Sarah!' I screamed as the car jerked to a full stop. Sarah shook her head with a pouty little smile and gave me a bye-bye wave as I slid off the Corvette's hood and stood aside.

In moments like that I pride myself on maintaining a calm, collected appearance. Imagine Spencer Tracy behind a double hit of Quaalude. I sauntered over to the curb and put Sarah's favourite calfskin boots down carefully side by side in the gutter, turned to watch the car's thundering acceleration away into the evening traffic. A cluster of onlookers stood on the sidewalk, bemused and curious as I walked through their mirage trying to whistle, certain, the way all fools are, that some new beginning lay back in the direction from which I had come.

Where Were You?

Hatch Covers

On my twenty-sixth birthday I shipped out of Newport News on the *Carib Founder.* She was a rusty Liberty ship refit under Liberian registry in the early 60s to carry general cargo between Europe and the Southeastern United States. I came aboard with the clothes I was wearing, a kid pouch for toiletries and documents and a second hand edition of Conrad's *Collected Works* I'd picked up at the Goodwill Shop next door to Sarah's flat in Montreal. I figured they'd have a Bible on board.

The night before we left I remember lying in my bunk absolutely terrified by the unfolding of my predictive curiosity and the potential for personal loss and disaster that seemed to lurk somewhere on the bleak ocean a week out of port. If the trip didn't jell, and change everything for the better, I'd know that something was fundamentally wrong with my schematized beliefs. In those days I took pride in the complexity of my premeditations, treating the world as if it was a column of figures.

The *Carib*'s officers were all Greek, the crew equal parts Spanish and Italian. With the exception of an aged Corsican in the radio shack, I was the only one on board who spoke English well enough to get beyond the weather. Our first destination was Barcelona where we were scheduled to off-load used farm machinery and pick up a transfer shipment of general cargo destined for the dock in Rotterdam. There, the captain would lay over for eight days awaiting further sailing instructions from the ship's agent in Piraeus.

While I had no official title on board it's easy enough to describe

my duties – I stood watch and I scraped off loose paint. Standing watch was easy, all I had to do was stand there and watch. Scraping off loose paint was another matter entirely. Once we were battened down and at sea it turned out it was my responsibility to stay at least a day's work ahead of a young Spanish oiler named Manuel Ortega who worked a split-shift between the engine room and the deck crew. Ortega, while at least five years my junior, was an obvious veteran with the mop-handled twelve-inch paint roller. From the first day out he never said a word to me, didn't even smile, and after a couple of shifts of this I realized there was some codified sense of honour at stake in his making the tasks of my rookie voyage as arduous as possible. Since I was the only one who ranked below Ortega on the ladder I was both the only one eligible for his job and the only one under his command. A bad spot in the food chain.

It quickly became apparent that the only way I could out-flank Ortega's frantic pace was to go out before breakfast and after dinner each day to scrape a hatch cover or two, which slowed him down because he had to forgo his twelve-inch roller and use a small brush, being careful not to clog the brass screw fittings with that lumpy grey enamel that covered every inch of the *Carib's* superstructure.

Between

The morning of the sixth day out I was on deck shortly after five trying to dip into a little Conrad before I set to work on that day's hatch cover. It was always exhilarating to be on deck early. As I read I watched the sky go through its slow dissolve, the gauze veil turning pink as it absorbed the infusions of sunrise, a fresh light that lifted the sea to sombre gaiety – like Beethoven on a tricycle. It was going to be another perfect day.

Suddenly, mysteriously, the deep-throated thrum of the engine changed pitch, slackened entirely and came to a full idle. I realized

we were coasting on the open ocean and felt a kind of awe, as if the familiar, moving panorama was about to become the actual, standing still place where we *were*. Above and behind me a door on the bridge banged open and the second officer came to the rail, shouted down to me: 'OLA! English! Look you! Crazy! *Crazy!*' pointing ahead off the starboard bow. I hopped to the rail, gaped with astonishment. There, a few hundred yards off across the glassy morning swell, was a closed over, double-ended dinghy, the topsides emblazoned with a bright red, white and blue Union Jack, the green and white BP trademark painted on the cowlings. A lone man sat amidships in a small oval cockpit, steadily feathering his craft toward us. Within minutes the *Carib*'s entire crew was assembled on deck, most of them sleepy-eyed and half-dressed, as the lone adventurer jockeyed his frail craft within hailing distance.

'Hallooo!' he called in a downtown British voice, 'Spragen de English? Parlato Anglaise?'

I looked around the deck and the other crew members nodded encouragement. 'I speak English!' I called down from the rail, a little exhilarated by this unexpected responsibility. 'How long you been goin'?'

The little bearded face smiled broadly: 'My one hundred and thirteenth day! Aiming for one-forty at Boston! Record's one-five-three!'

'No kidding!' I called. 'Need anything?'

The tiny bobbing row boat was directly abeam now. 'No thanks! By Guinness Rule one isn't permitted resupply! No worry – stores are tip-top! Any news I should know about? One gets damned hungry for the telly!'

I thought quickly. 'Did you hear about Kennedy?'

'Which?' he back-pedalled his dinghy as it began to fall astern.

'Kennedy!' I yelled, 'The politician! Did you hear what happened?'

'Oh no! Not something awful I hope!'

'Bad enough.' I took a deep breath, realizing the message as he would receive it, 'He drowned his secretary!'

'Really!' The little man stammered, shaking his head, visibly perturbed, '*Really,* my goodness. How *dreadful*.'

'They're still investigating! You'll hear all about it when you get to Boston!' I gave him a big double-handed wave and the rest of the crew followed suit, shouting, 'Bravo! Adios! Good luck!'

The litle man acknowledged us with a modest nod and sat back down to his oars, stroking off at a brisk pace as if one way or another we'd all meet again shortly, no matter our various outcomes. The captain gave him two forlorn *bloots* of hail and farewell on the big steam horn, the only time in the whole voyage I heard it used, and then we too were underway, the bells clanging back and forth between bridge and boiler room, the frail row boat slipping astern more quickly than one would have imagined.

For a long time I watched the point on the horizon where that lone oarsman had been. Wondering all the things one wonders about in those moments, neither here nor there, but between.

care

Spotting: a case history

The Purchase

It all started the day I paid fifty bucks for a new pair of corduroy pants, marked down from seventy-five, at Holt Renfrew. It was a case of impulse shopping. The kind of thing I do sometimes when I'm depressed. In truth, it was the first occasion in a couple of years that I hadn't shopped second-hand. The only reason I ducked into the ritzy store on Bloor Street was that it was snowing hard and the big red JANUARY SALE signs invited my eyes past the revolving doors into the dense throng of shoppers. I decided that battling a crowd of real people might take my mind off things.

I went inside.

A scene of frontier bedlam! Every aisle in the store was packed shoulder to shoulder with well-dressed men trying on suit jackets, sport coats, sweaters and bathrobes, while others stood three-deep around tables piled high with designer-brand shirts, or groped up to their shoulders into the big tubs of socks and underwear.

It took me a couple of minutes to work my way into the throng and every garment I managed to pull free was either a forty-six short or tailored for a double-knit lifestyle I found more than alien. Then I saw them – a mauve corduroy pant, nice weight cotton, a good roomy cut in the leg. In a kind of remote-control trance I watched myself put down fifty bucks at the cash register and go to stand in front of facing mirrors so a little Italian guy could pin up my cuffs and chalk alterations to the ass.

At this point in the story I should digress to explain something. For the last little while I've had a *minor* problem with spotting. Without being indelicate, I'm referring to those tell-tale damp

circles that periodically appear around the crotch of tight pants, particularly if I spend most of the day sitting down with my legs crossed, which I often do. Believe me, these damp spots are nothing you'd notice unless I mentioned it, although if I've had an especially long day in light-coloured trousers you might think I'd spilled a little tea in my lap or something. I'm only aware of it once or twice a week myself, as in: 'Gee, I guess I've been sitting *there* a long time.'

Sarah, whom I live with, was pretty used to it too – aside from casual references in connection with a couple of instances of drunken bedwetting up at the cabin I'd never even heard her mention 'spotting.'

All of that changed after I bought the new corduroys. They fit snugger than the blue wool navy pants I normally wore in winter and, according to Sarah, they looked great on me. Feeling a little guilty about spending so much money on clothes I wore my new corduroys three days straight. When I got home after work on the third day Sarah watched me take off my coat, then gasped and giggled. I looked down, a little stunned, and – wouldn't you know it – there was a large light-coloured semi-circle on the front of my new pants! Well, you can imagine how angry I was. Fifty bucks I could hardly afford and my new cords already had a stain next to the zipper. I took the pants off immediately and gave the whole area a thorough scrubbing with soap and hot water, then hung them on a rad to dry. A bothersome chore, but obviously worth the trouble.

First thing next morning I took my new cords off the rad to see how they'd dried. I couldn't believe my eyes! The stained area had dried a full shade *lighter* than the surrounding cloth. This had never happened to me before – it meant an emergency trip to Royal Cleaners. What the heck, I thought, that's okay, a cleaning will probably help break them in. But when my fifty-dollar cords came back from Royal Cleaners the blond patch at the crotch was

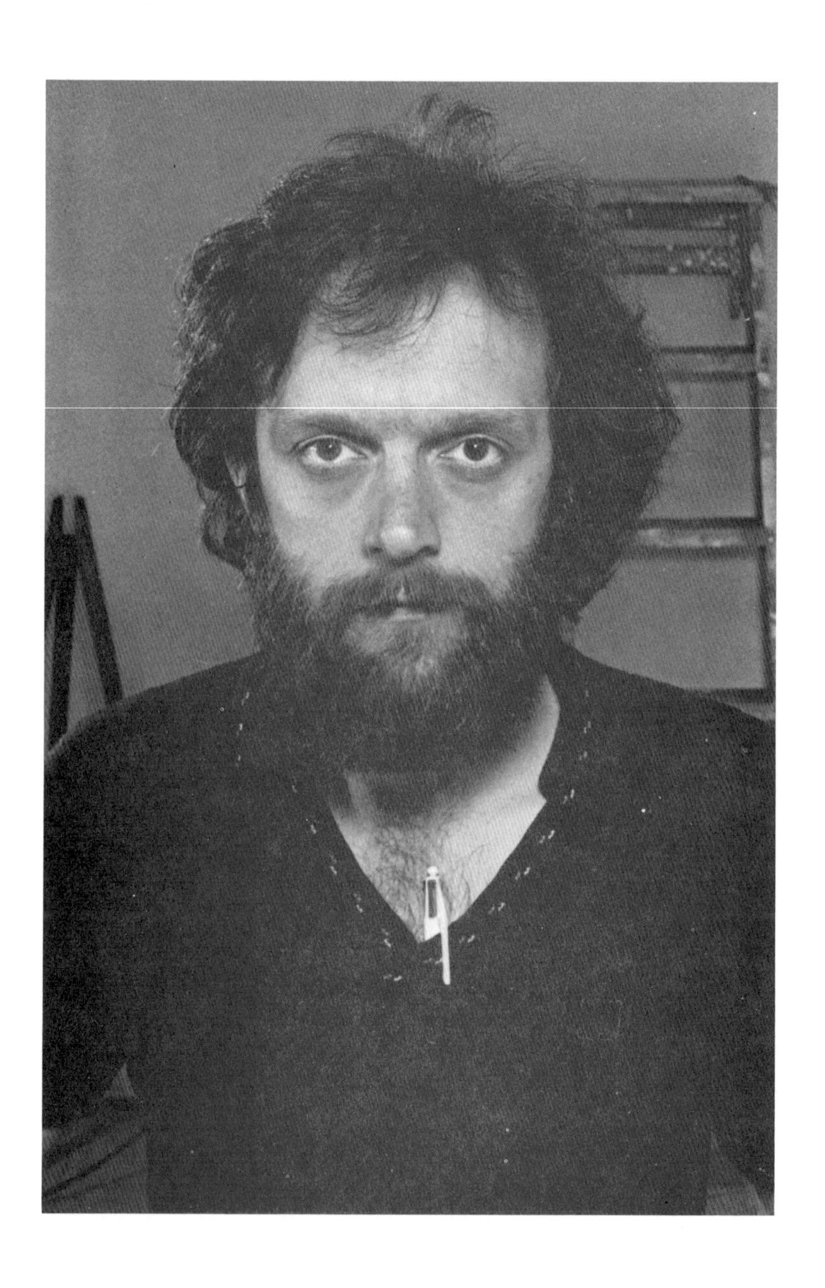

not only still there, but more crisply defined, a permanent testament to my spotting. Unbelievable!

I was so damn mad that I decided to take those cords straight back to Holt Renfrew and demand a refund. Something's got to be wrong when a supposedly top-notch men's clothier charges seventy-five bucks regular price for a pair of corduroys that won't even stand up to three days' normal wear. There had to be government standards for the strength of dye they used in men's pants. Undoubtedly, Holt Renfrew had ignored it, probably trying to cut a corner and make a few extra bucks. No way I was gonna stand still for that! While I'd never actually discussed the matter with other men, I *knew* I wasn't alone – spotting was as common as receding hair, untalked about certainly, but common none the less. If Holt Renfrew wanted to pretend they didn't know about spotting it was high time someone brought the matter front and centre. The way I saw it, those snobby little poofs behind the counter probably figured they were safe – I mean, what well-heeled customer of *theirs* would care to proclaim his spotting by returning a pair of poorly-dyed slacks? Well, this time they'd picked the wrong guy. I made up my mind to take those cords back to Holt Renfrew as soon as I had a spare minute. I'd raise hell with the manager. If it got down to the short strokes I was ready to embarrass him in front of a store-full of customers.

The Prostrate

One morning a couple of weeks later Sarah watched me put on my new corduroys, then take them off again.

'Don't you like your new pants?'

'They're okay,' I said, 'a bit tight.'

'It's too bad about that stain – '

'I know,' I said, 'it's really a drag. Maybe if I soaked them overnight in Javex they'd all turn the same colour – '

'I think you should see somebody about it.' Sarah spoke routinely and I answered the same way.

'Don't worry, I'm gonna raise *hell* with the head guy at Holt's.'

'I'm not talking about the corduroys. I'm talking about your dribbling.'

'Are you serious? That's spotting! There's nothing you can do about *that.* It's just the prostrate acting up – '

'That's pro*state.*'

'Right, prostate.'

'Well, D'arcy mentioned it the other night when you were having a nap. He thinks you should have it looked at by a doctor.'

'D'arcy talked to you about *my* spotting?' D'arcy was our next-door neighbour. She had to be kidding.

Sarah nodded seriously: 'I'm afraid so. He's noticed the stains on your pants and he says you might have a low-grade kidney infection.'

'Oh, horseballs!' I said, knowing there were at least a few things in life I was certain about. I pulled the cords back on roughly, brushed at the lighter patch near my crotch. 'It's only spotting, for crissakes. *All* men have it. I'm lucky to have it so light.'

'Why don't I ask Betty about it.' Betty was the feminist nurse downstairs.

'Go right ahead,' I said, calling her bluff, 'just for the heck of it. Betty'll tell you all about spotting.'

A half-hour later I found out that fifty percent of men over sixty have prostate problems and it's fairly common among younger men as well. According to Betty I most likely had a low-grade kidney infection that they'd clean up in a few weeks with sulfa drugs. If that didn't work they'd run a barium test on my kidneys and if *that* didn't show anything it might be diabetes and I'd likely have to stay overnight in a hospital so they could do a full work-up. But it was probably nothing to worry about. Betty pointed out that there was a family health unit a couple of blocks away where I could

go and make an appointment. They'd check out the problem in no time. After listening to Sarah I considered the matter briefly and then said sure – there was no point walking around with a low-grade kidney infection and, when I thought about it, the spotting had been going on for at least five years, if not longer.

The Examination

The very next morning, a Monday, I dropped by the Family Practice Unit to see about arranging an appointment. The receptionist immediately gave me a clipboard with a routine questionnaire attached to it and directed me to a chair in the waiting room. The place was empty except for an elderly Portuguese lady dressed all in black. I'd barely finished printing my name when the receptionist reappeared and told me a doctor would see me right away. Boy, this place was efficient!

I went out into the corridor and shook hands with a petite, surprisingly young and pretty lady doctor in a white lab coat. Marvellous lively eyes. She led me back and around a corner to her office – a very small room with the standard couch covered with white paper from a roll, some cupboards, a sink, a little desk with a mirror above it and two chairs.

The young woman glanced at my unfinished forms and put the clipboard quickly aside. 'You can finish up the questionnaire later. What seems to be the problem?'

'Oh, nothing major,' I said, 'I've noticed a little spotting the last month or two – I know there's probably nothing you can do about it, but – ?'

'Spotting?' Her brow furrowed, 'what do you mean?'

'Oh, you know, spots on my pants – a leaky gasket.'

Flat faced: 'You mean incontinence?'

'Yeah, I suppose so, but in a *very* minor way.'

The young woman watched her tapping fingers for a moment

and then drilled her attention straight into my eyes.

'Any discomfort when you pass water?'

'None.'

'Discharge?'

'Oh no, nothing like that.'

'Blood in the urine?'

'Nope.'

'Any history of venereal disease?'

'Never.'

'Hernia?'

'No.'

'Any history of prostate problems in the family?'

'Not that I know of – ' That was sure a guess.

'Bedwetting?'

'Heavens no.'

'Do you wake up to pass water in the night?'

'Yup.'

'How often?'

'Oh, only once. Never more than twice.'

'Mm-hm,' she looked at the clipboard again, 'Well, I guess we'll need a sample.'

Boy, was she fast! I followed her out into the hall, around the corner and past the little Portuguese lady in the waiting room. The young doctor opened the bathroom door for me and disappeared, came back a moment later with a stainless steel tray, on it two stainless steel cups, and a gauze patch.

'Wipe the opening with the swab, pass a little urine into the first cup and then put the rest of it into the other cup. We don't want the first part, understand?'

'Sure,' I chirped, taking the tray and closing the door, 'no problem.'

There was a problem though. I'd already gone to the bathroom that morning. After a couple of minutes of unrewarded contraction I ran the hot water tap and put my hand under it, remembering the trick from camp. I was partially successful, although it didn't look like nearly enough for a full-scale test. I carried the sample tray back past the little Portuguese lady and around the corner to the young woman's office.

'Which is the second part?' she asked.

I'd completely forgotten about that end of it so I guessed the emptier of the two cups: 'Is that enough?'

'It should be. Take a seat, I'll be right back.' She disappeared and I went back to the questionnaire on my clipboard, just starting to fill in the details of my medical history when the doctor returned, closing the door behind her.

'Could you lower your pants, please, and sit up on the couch?'

'Sure thing,' I said easily, wondering in a giddy rush if I'd remembered to put on underwear.

A lucky break.

The young woman stood in front of me and, once I was sitting down, pointed to a damp spot on the front of my under-shorts. 'Is this the extent of your problem?'

'Yeah, that's about it,' I said. 'I-I don't even know why I'm – '

'Could you lower your underpants for me, please?'

I did that.

The young woman probed my groin with two fingers and asked me to cough several times and speak up if I felt any discomfort. I did what I was told and kept my attention focused in the mirror on the opposite wall, my face showing nothing as the young woman fondled my genitals.

She left off her examination abruptly and went to the cupboard beside the mirror, talking as she searched the shelves.

'Could you take your pants and your underpants right off, please. I want to do a rectal examination ... to check the prostate ... hmmm, doesn't seem to be any petroleum jelly here. I'll be back in a moment – '

I waited until she was gone and then took my pants off and put them over a chair back. In the adjoining examination room I could make out some kind of muffled conversation, the voices heightened in an artificial way, as if amplified. I moved closer to the sink to listen but couldn't decipher what was being discussed. While I was in front of the mirror I took the opportunity to do a close check on the two little red dots on the tip of my nose. I'd had these dots for years, apparently they had something to do with getting repeatedly sunburned, but they sort of looked like dormant pimples. Close inspection revealed that they hadn't changed for the worse, although they had been getting more pronounced lately. Again, I promised myself that someday when I had the extra money I'd have those dots surgically removed – in the meantime they didn't look all that bad.

When the doctor came back I went straight over to the couch opposite the mirror and sat down.

'That's fine, now could you lie down on your left side facing the wall and bring your knees up to your chest? That's it, bring them right up to the chest.'

I listened to the young woman unwrap a plastic glove and snap it on, spin the lid off a jar. A pause. In one motion she slid two fingers up my rectum, shoved them in as far as they'd go and began to rotate, checking all the walls of the cavity. Then, just as quickly, she withdrew her fingers, peeled off the rubber glove and whapped it into the wastebasket. The whole thing took about ten seconds, just long enough for a return trip to Mars. I sat upright and smiled into the mirror on the opposite wall as she washed her hands vigorously under hot water and towelled them dry. I felt pretty good, kind of light-headed, and it showed in my face. No more hurdles left until they put in the catheter, and that was a long way off.

'Well?'

The young woman spun the top back on the jelly jar and turned to me: 'Everything quite normal. No swelling or distension of the

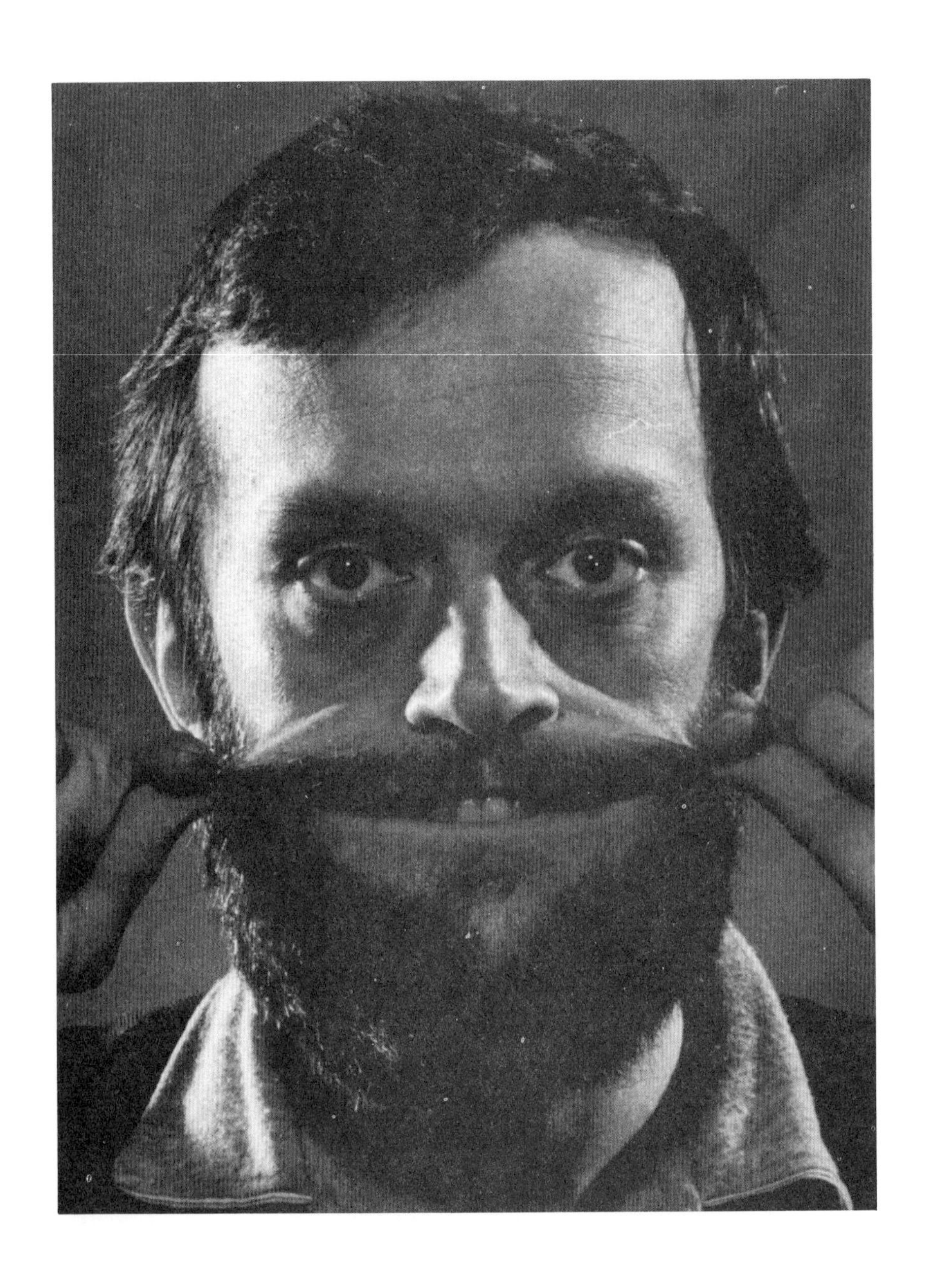

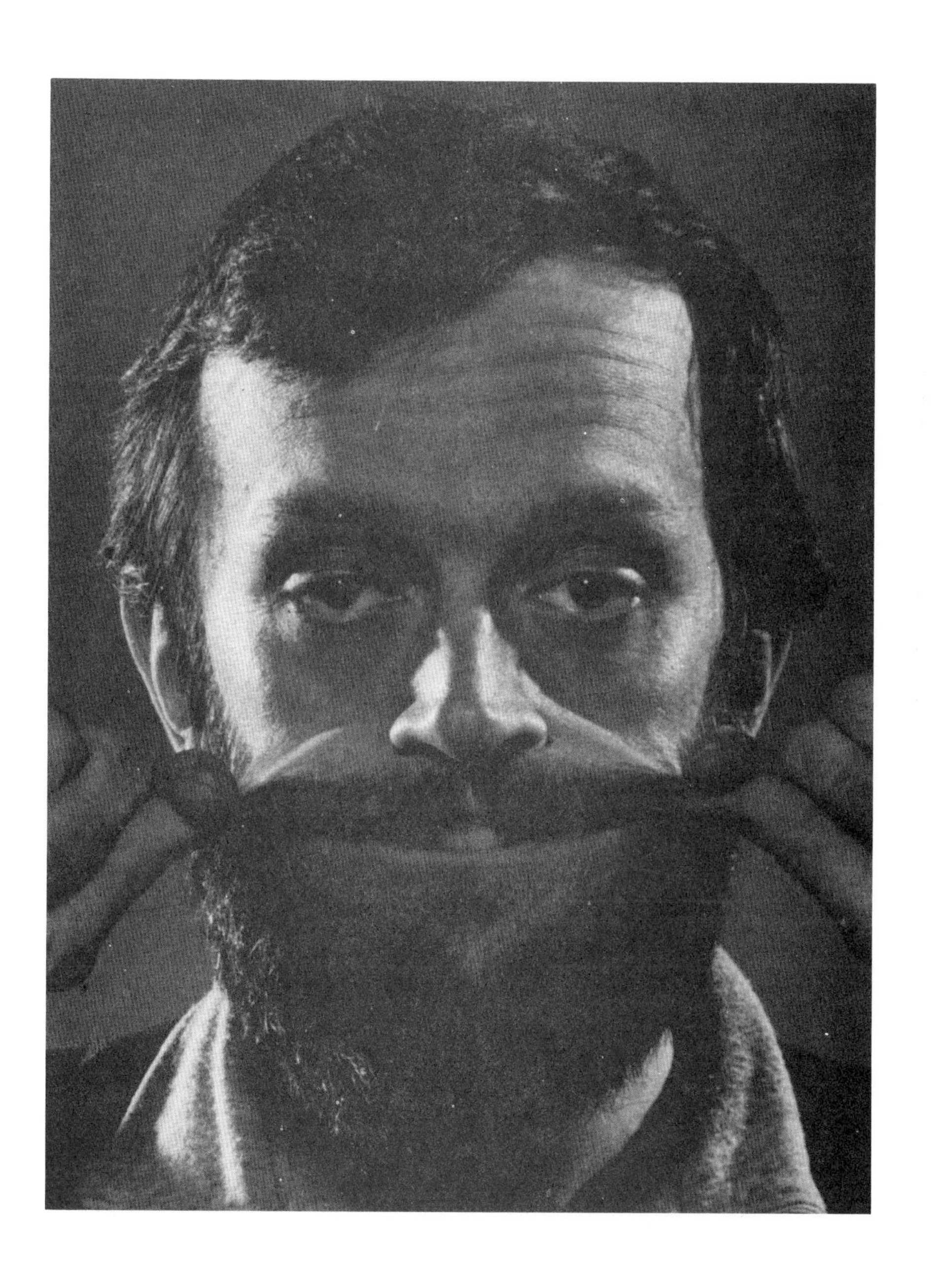

prostate. You can put your pants back on now. I'll check your specimen with the lab and be back in a minute.'

I started to get dressed, felt the greasy lubricant between my buttocks, and used a paper towel to swab it away. I threw the paper towel in the wastebasket, thought better of it, and bunched it into the pocket of my parka to be dealt with later. Alone in the room again, I listened to that baffled conversation through the wall and then sat down at the little table and began working on my questionnaire. I breezed through the whole thing in a couple of minutes, answering no to almost everything, and then began to read the first paragraph of a typewritten sheet that was scotch-taped to the clipboard.

It read:

GENERAL INFORMATION FOR PATIENTS

The Family Practice Unit is a teaching unit of the University of Toronto Department of Family and Community Medicine. In addition to providing comprehensive health care to people of any age, it prepares postgraduate students for careers in family medicine. The interns being taught at the Family Practice Unit may participate in your care. Student participation in your care is supervised by staff physicians, sometimes behind one-way mirrors ...

Wha-a-a!

Before I could even think about that my young doctor returned with a middle-aged oriental lady in a white lab coat.

'Hello,' she said in a very familiar voice. 'I'm Dr Chan.'

We shook hands and Dr Chan smiled a beatific smile, indicating her younger companion. 'Well, Dr Duke has done all the routine tests. Your urine is completely normal and there's no enlargement of the prostate.'

'I know,' I said. 'I didn't really expect you to pin it down. I guess it's one of those things I'll have to learn to live with – '

'Well, not entirely,' Dr Chan said, that inscrutable smile again.

'This kind of occurrence often has more to do with stress. What do you do for a living?'

'I'm a writer,' I said.

Dr Chan nodded agreeably. 'You're under stress from time to time?'

'Oh, sure, but no more than the next guy. Never had any psychosomatic problems – I mean, I think I know quite a bit about myself and – ' my voice trailed off.

'Yes, I see,' Dr Chan massaged her little finger. 'All I can suggest is that you try to limit your intake of fluids – simply limit the physical amount that your kidneys have to deal with,' a careful smile, 'and try to cope with your daily stress as *openly* as possible. Even for myself it's quite often difficult to pinpoint how emotional problems affect my body, so often things that are suppressed surface in some other way, you know?'

'Sure,' I said jovially, getting up and moving toward my coat. 'And if that doesn't work, what? A diaper?' I laughed nervously, parka in hand, the door half open, but Dr Chan's smile only flickered.

'Perhaps a mild tranquillizer – '

I laughed again, said: 'Gee, let's hope not,' and waved goodbye to Dr Duke, her part almost forgotten in the rush of prognosis. 'Thanks very much, Dr Chan, sorry to have bothered you – '

Both she and Dr Duke nodded with their arms crossed and watched me bump into the door frame on my way out.

STEEL

Of Mice and Men

Albino Cockroaches

On April 21, 1979 – in the first limpid hour of dawn – I found myself behind the wheel of a silver Buick Centurion streaking south through the citrus groves of central California. I was heading for the Baja Peninsula, trying to follow through on the first real challenge that had appealed to me in over a year. My plan was to drive straight south to Tijuana, cross into Mexico, then follow the inland coast of the peninsula for 150 miles until I arrived on the desolate shore of the Canal de las Ballenas. Once there I'd park, sleep in the back seat of the car for a few hours – then I'd get up, strip down to my boxers and try to find a shady, elevated spot that provided a panoramic view of the shallow water between the mainland and Angel de la Garda, an off-shore island. With luck my arrival on that mile or so of arid shoreline would coincide with the shallow water breeding rituals which capped the grey whales' annual 12,000-mile migration down the coast from Alaska. After watching the grey whales copulate for about six hours I'd hop back in the car and retrace my steps north to the Los Angeles area.

In Toronto, three days earlier, I'd agreed to deliver the Centurion to a Dr Elaine Chan in Glendale. If I was more than twenty-four hours late Dr Chan was legally obliged to notify the highway patrol. Obviously I was running on a tight schedule – the time tolerances had to be shaved razor-thin.

With various hitch-hikers helping out behind the wheel I'd managed to keep Dr Chan's car on the road for fifty hours straight, crossing the Nevada line with a comfortable cushion which, barring the unforeseen, would allow me to make my commando raid on the

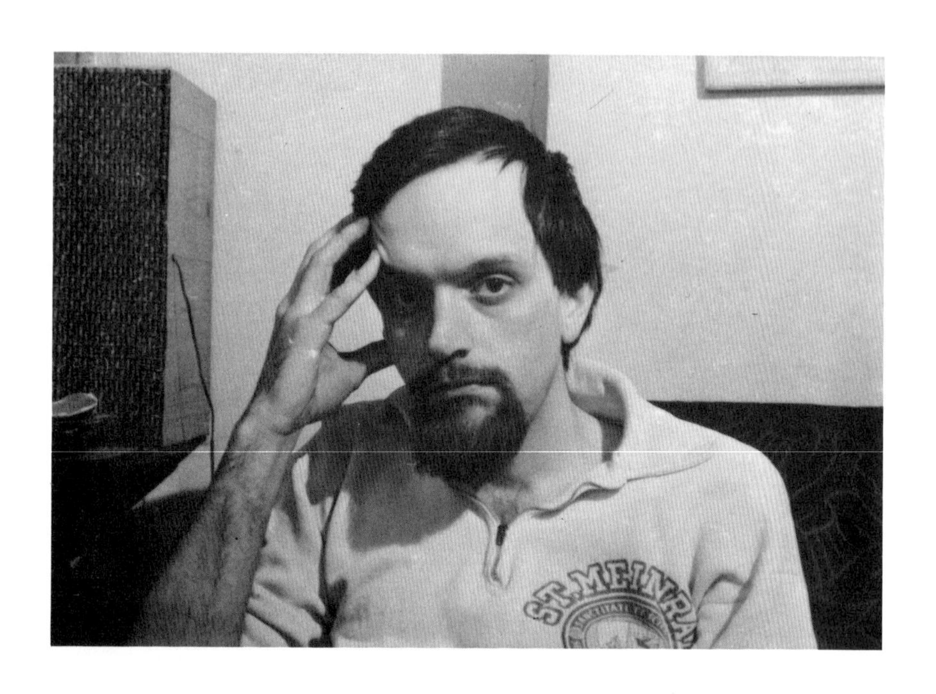
ST.MEINRA

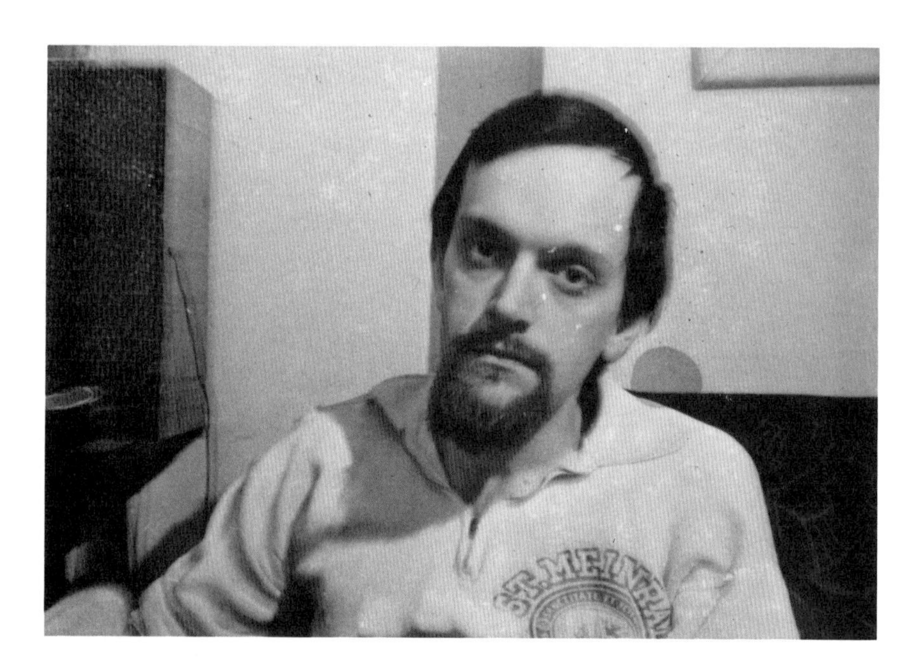
ST.MEINRA

grey whales in Baja without jeopardizing the delivery date.

Why grey whales? There's no logical answer to that question. I vaguely remember overhearing people at a dinner party discussing a television special they'd seen the previous evening. Something about Jacques Cousteau riding his jet sled down into the gloomy depths of the Pacific. The harsh television lights suddenly illuminating the tail flukes of a boxcar-sized mammal. Barnacles big as your fist glowing neon blue as the landscape of ancient, battle-torn hide undulates past the camera. Then helicopter shots of their ponderous foreplay, the enormous beasts lolling beside *Calypso* in the turquoise shallows of a Baja lagoon, thick jets of sperm staining the water milk white, hundreds of eco-freaks looking on from the shore, strumming guitars, thumping bongo drums, hully-gullying around diminishing campfires late into the night.

On the other hand, it may well be that I simply wanted to escape from myself for a few days and happened to find grey whales and drive-away cars mentioned side by side in the newspaper – the choice made for me the moment I identified it – like it happens with the *I Ching*.

To be honest, it's impossible to remember precisely what kind of stimulation I was after in those days, the inner pressures that made me act the way I did. At bottom, I was obsessed with the thought that, although the world was about to explode, the human species would somehow prevail, mutate further back toward thick-browed ignorance, snow white cockroaches flourishing in the core of a nuclear reactor. Hold onto that kind of apocalyptic world-view for long enough and the only thing left to believe in is anti-climax.

Looking back on it from this elevation, the entire Baja episode seems utterly improbable, a kamikaze thrust toward some impossible coincidence that, even had it clicked, would have resolved nothing. But that's how I was in those days. Jumbled up almost all the time, trying to fill my life with whatever was close at hand because

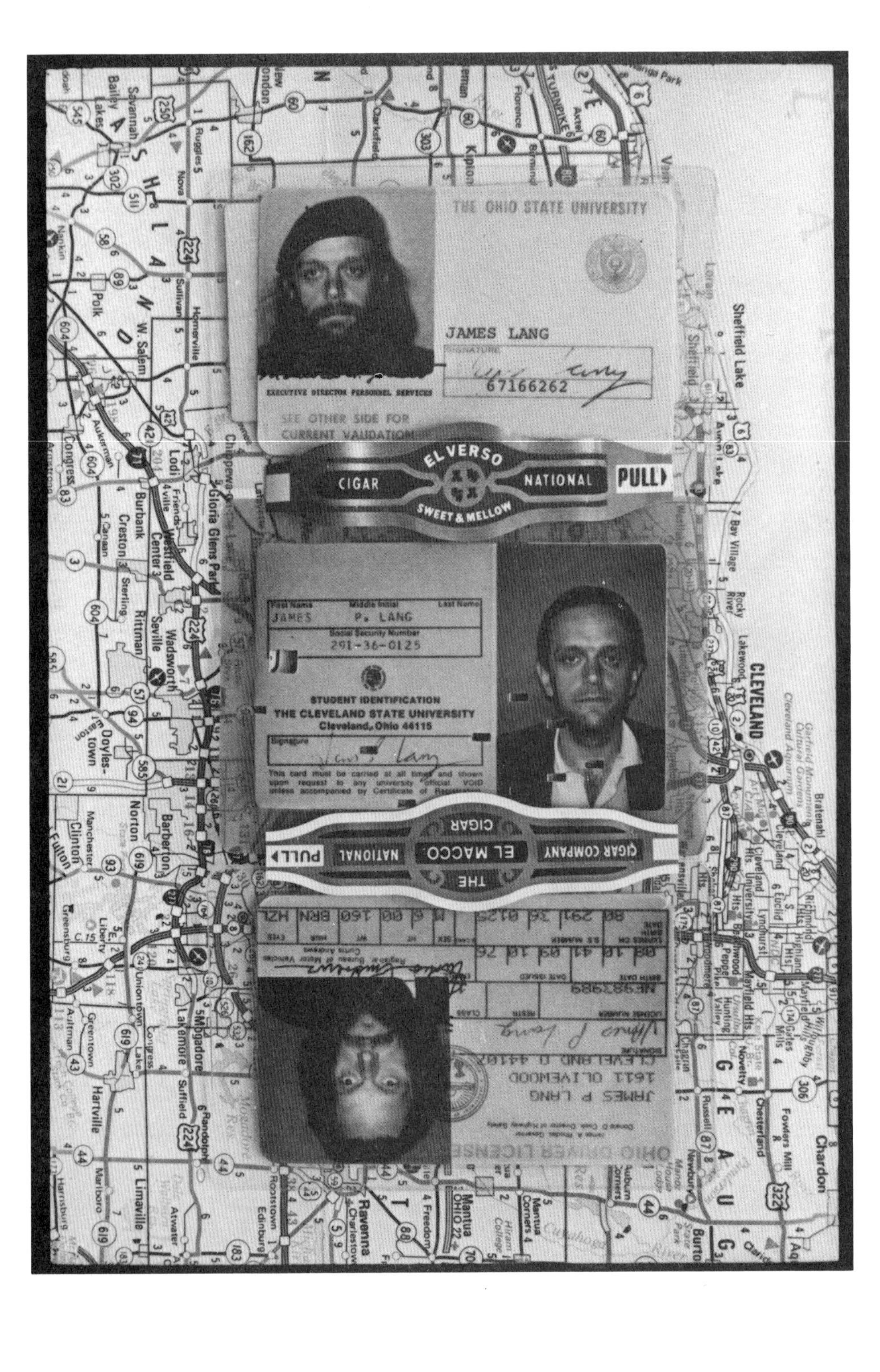

THE OHIO STATE UNIVERSITY
JAMES LANG
SIGNATURE
67166262
EXECUTIVE DIRECTOR PERSONNEL SERVICES
SEE OTHER SIDE FOR CURRENT VALIDATION
EL VERSO
CIGAR
NATIONAL
SWEET & MELLOW
PULL
First Name Middle Initial Last Name
JAMES P. LANG
Social Security Number
291-36-0125
STUDENT IDENTIFICATION
THE CLEVELAND STATE UNIVERSITY
Cleveland, Ohio 44115
Signature
THE
EL MACCO
CIGAR
NATIONAL
CIGAR COMPANY
PULL
OHIO DRIVER LICENSE
JAMES P LANG
1611 OLIVEWOOD
CLEVELAND O 44107
CLEVELAND

that seemed the simplest way to deal with 'the issues,' trying to do everything real *fast* to stay ahead of a sadness that ate people for breakfast. According to my beliefs the act of living was something like ripping off a wet Band-aid – the faster you did it the less it hurt, the sooner it healed.

A Hint of Fizz

Crossing Nevada the previous evening I'd drunk a fair amount of beer, let the young Mormon hitch-hiker I'd picked up on the outskirts of Salt Lake City cannonball us across the desert while I scanned the Bible-thumping Baptists on the AM radio. We must've stopped at least a dozen times so I could get out and piss on that griddle-hot desert. A hundred billion stars throbbing overhead. The kind of over-amped memory that sticks with you for life, popping into your head every time you hear the words 'desert' and 'piss' used in the same sentence. It's no wonder that men born and raised in those parts have taken to wearing embroidered silk shirts and high heels. One way or another a guy's gotta cope. But back to our story.

Early on the morning of this account, the Nevada line two hours back, the young Mormon who'd been driving shook me awake to say goodbye. He showed me where we were on the map – the Barstow Interchange – said all I had to do was stay on Route 56 South and I'd be on the outskirts of Los Angeles by lunch, hit the Tijuana border crossing two hours after that. Somewhat groggily I got behind the wheel, realizing that I now had to hold the 70 mph pace at all costs because the official clock was running down. I had just over two days to rendezvous with the grey whales a thousand miles to the south and then reconnect the odometer to deke back up and drop the Centurion off at Dr Chan's place in Glendale.

For the next hour I drove without thinking. My mind could have gone almost anywhere during that period but it stayed pretty much around the car, which is lucky for us, because around mid-morning I picked up a young woman hitch-hiking at the San Bernadino Interchange. She got into the car without saying a word, or even looking at me, and rolled a cigarette as I pulled back into the traffic. I noticed that she had a small butterfly tattooed high on her left arm, watched out of the corner of my eye while she fiddled with the radio until she found a country & western station that pleased her. Finally:

'Got a name?'

Her eyes darted across to meet mine, chisel-hard, then away again. I could call her Sarah if I liked. She waited, smoking her cigarette. I'm coming off a bad scene in West Texas, she said. You might as well know that right off. In case the troopers stop you for something. Sure, I said, No problem. What happened? She eyed me with hostile bravura. I got fucked by six guys in a police station is what happened. If it's all the same to you I'd just as soon stay away from the cops for awhile.

I nodded agreeably and tried to keep my eyes on the highway ahead of us.

'Where you from?'

Nowhere, she said. A bunch of different trailer parks. Her father was in the army. That was about it. She asked me if she could drink one of the warm beers and I said sure. For the next hour I drove and listened while she finished the last three cans. She was looking for a drummer in a rock band who'd stopped answering her letters. But that was okay. She knew the bars in L.A. where The Roosters had gigs. If her money ran out before she found him she'd easily pick up a job dancing in one of the clubs.

She said she was hungry so I exited into a little town and pulled up in front of a diner.

She sat at the counter and ordered two cheeseburgers. She said that she trusted me and she didn't know why. For some reason I was real easy to talk to, like we'd known each other for years. I said I felt that way too, it was like I didn't have to explain anything to her. She studied me, chewing a mouthful of cheeseburger, her eyes buzzing around, adjusting to something they'd just discovered in my face. I know what it is, she said. She ate faster now, talking while she swallowed. Something about my eyes reminded her of her twin brother, the one who'd joined the Marines and come back from Viet Nam with both his forearms gone. They'd issued him stainless steel pincers but he'd left them in an alley, preferring the classic look of black kid leather over high-impact styrene. There was no way two people could've been any closer than Sarah and her twin brother. It practically drove her nuts to see what they'd done to him. I asked how she meant that. She said it sounded dumb. He'd come home with a smile that was too big. In the months that followed, he smiled so indiscriminately that the expression stopped meaning anything. He grinned all the time, like a jackass eating bull thistle, no matter what was going on around him. He even grinned when he was fast asleep.

'You think I'm kidding,' she said.

'No,' I said, 'I know exactly what you're talking about. So what happened?'

You wouldn't believe me if I told you, the woman named Sarah said, sipping her coffee, lighting a fresh cigarette from the butt she had going. Six months after he came home from Nam her twin brother had swallowed a tiny crescent of glass that somehow calved off a beer bottle he was swigging at this wedding reception. Died from internal bleeding before the doctors could get that little sliver of glass out of his gut. Doctors said it was a freak accident. No fuckin way. Not after she'd crept into his room late at night and found that grin splattered across his face. I started to say something but she told me to shut up. Fuck it, she said. Fuck the whole shot. Then she started to giggle and, realizing that that was how she dealt with it, I began to giggle too, her response so plausible that I found myself in it. Everyone in the restaurant was staring at us.

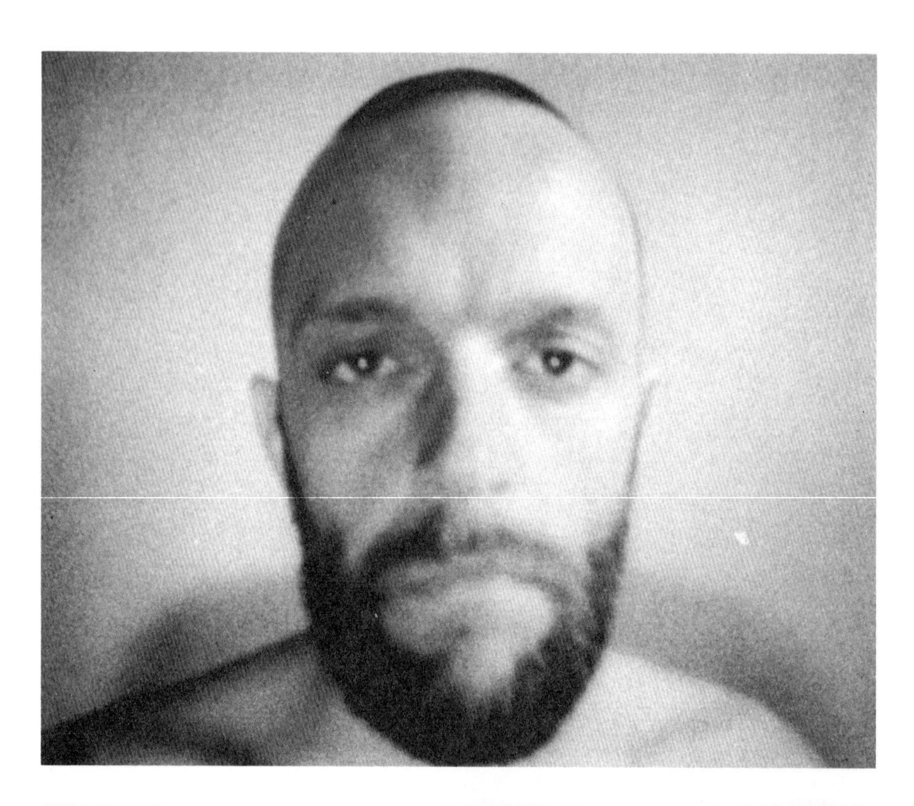

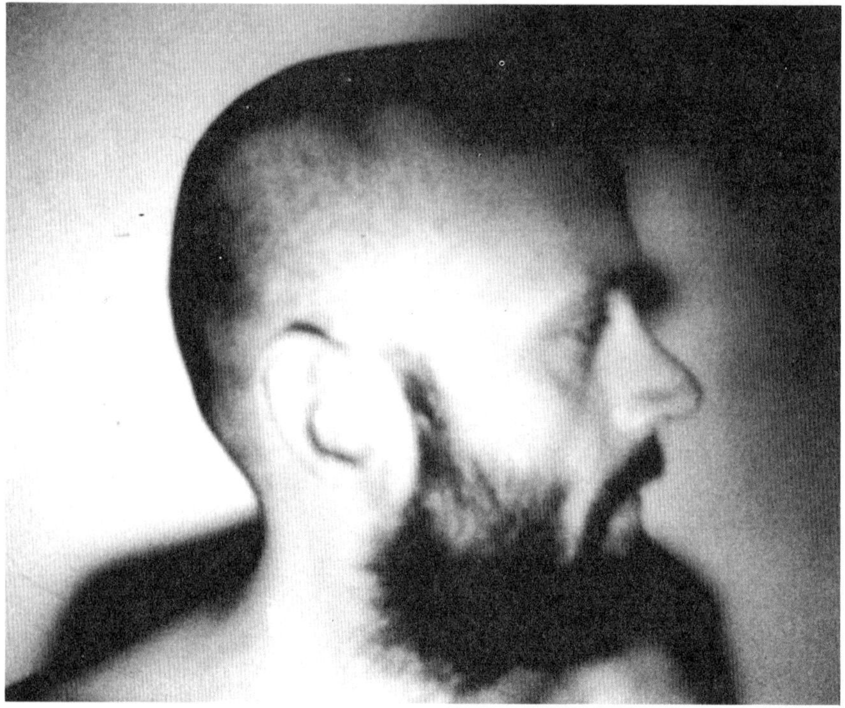

As we swung back onto the expressway she said it was my turn to talk. We opened fresh cans of beer as I warmed to the practised recitation of all the people I thought I was, could have been, were it not for the fact that all the roads had been left untaken, like Robert Frost with a bum knee. That still qualifies as a road, she said, and I nodded. The Unroad. She laughed at that and asked me where I was headed, sipped her beer while I ran down whatever justifications I was using at the time to explain my improbable dash across the continent to squat on a stretch of desert shoreline and watch the sexual congress of grey whales. She said she'd dealt with people who were into abstract trips like that, people who probably thought like I did. Shitheads, as she called us.

By the time we'd finished off the first cold six-pack the woman named Sarah was pretty much convinced that she might as well accompany me on my head-long blitz to the Canal de las Ballenas. There was no big rush about finding her old boyfriend. It'd only been a so-so thing to begin with. Next week would be just as good as this week.

'And you might even see grey whales making love in *shallow* water!' I added.

'*Really!*' she replied, nodding her head energetically, the way she did whenever the agreement got too big. At that point it was pretty clear that there was some fizz in the water between us.

Enter the Strobe

By noon we were nearing Santa Ana – windows down, radio up, air conditioner roaring, a fresh supply of beer on the front seat between us – our conversation flying all over the place as we made bounce-pass connections with the crazy unnatural spectacles out there on the roadside. Like:

WHITTIER

NEXT EXIT

'Whittier! Big Dick!'

'Right! Whittier College! The giant turkey on the pedestal!'

The garish colours blowing by our open windows, the whole sorrowful world rippling and popping like a flag in the wind of our passing – a kaleidoscopic display for us, and us alone. Then, miraculously:

ANAHEIM NEXT FOUR EXITS

DISNEYLAND FOLLOW RTE 7

Whooo-*weee!* Unbee-lievable! Sarah and I bounced up and down on the front seat like kids. This was a one-shot chance we simply *couldn't* afford to pass up. What the hell! We had close to two days for the Baja thing, Disneyland would only take a couple of hours – why not?

I roared up the exit ramp at Route 7 and we stopped at the first roadhouse to buy another six-pack of Coors. In my heart I knew that if I drank even a couple more I was going to be in serious trouble by the middle of the afternoon. But that didn't disturb me, not in the least. What the heck, eh? This was California! I was following my nose! We were on a sky's-the-limit, rip-roaring wing-ding! This was *exactly* the right thing to be doing. Graft an enamelled memory of Disneyland onto a tattooed girl named Sarah. Pour the essence into the shaft of an arrow and release it ahead into the fluttering strobe of time. The arrow thumping to ground at my feet years later, the shaft quivering to rest. A violin only I would hear.

The Patented Finishing Hold

It seemed to take us ages to find an empty parking spot in the vast sprawl of the Disneyland lot but Sarah and I didn't give a shit. We were drinking ice-cold Coors and we could see the minaretted towers of a fantastic fairy castle thrusting up above distant trees. As soon as we found a vacant slot we rolled up all the windows so the

Centurion's air conditioner could cool us down while we finished the last four cans of beer. In a few minutes we'd be face to face with that epoxy hippo we'd seen on television as kids. Not to mention Annette Funicello's incredible tits! Hey, what a boffo trip!

The instant I stepped outside the air-conditioned sedan I realized that I was in Red Alert Trouble, about to stall and pitch backwards into a death spin. I was standing in a steep-sided furnace, the sun's blazing dazzle focusing in on me from ten thousand windshields. I sagged to my knees in the shadow of the Buick but Sarah came around and insisted that I stand up – draped my arm around her shoulder and began literally dragging me down an endless aisle of cars toward the distant gate. When we were almost there I stumbled off to one side and puked my guts out. Bent over like that in the insufferable heat, gagging and panting and spitting beside someone's station wagon, I tasted my own sour taste and began to feel very, very sad.

Sarah stood off a few feet, watching, then came to help me. I could barely walk but somehow she dragged me along, supporting me tight around the waist while we shuffled into the dense pack of squealing, impatient kids that surrounded the ticket booth. While we waited our turn Sarah did her best to cheer me up, but nothing worked. In the raw violence of my self-pity I knew we were about to walk through the Gates of Hell and enter a zone of glowing malignancy. I remember saying: 'It's like we have parasites in our blowholes,' but by then it was too late. We were inside the park on a wide, flower-lined boulevard – a Champs-Elysées of childhood fantasy – boxed in on all sides by family pods doing their best to stay together in the crush.

As occasionally happens, the last increment of alcohol I'd absorbed had triggered a new and unexpected biochemical equilibrium. All at once, the world around me snapped back into razor-sharp black and white focus. I was suddenly experiencing something that was parallel to real life, only a bit slower. I realized *exactly*

where I was. Exactly *who* I was. Exactly who *Sarah* was. Why we were walking in the same direction as all these strange people. Why the fantastic spires of a feudal castle beckoned at the end of our boulevard. My face went numb, began to meld in time-lapse transition, my eyebrows thickening together like Spencer Tracy's in *Dr Jekyll & Mr Hyde.* (Note: This condition is too often referred to as 'a black-out,' a loaded phrase which implies diminished perceptual acuity. More accurately, this mode of consciousness should be understood as John Q. Public's only access to out-of-the-body experience. A readily available psychic episode characterized by infinitely clear perceptions which totally bypass the memory hopper.)

Suddenly, the children ahead of us squealed and surged forward. A huge mouse walking upright like a man was angling into the crowded flow of the boulevard from a side street. He offered his white-gloved hands to the little kids, his high-pitched voice distant and muffled: 'Hi there! Hi there, boys and girls! Hi there! Hi there!'

The back of the mouse's enormous head bobbed high above the throng of kids a few yards in front of me and I quickened my pace a little, edging up on him through the minnowing mob like a German U-boat. Finally, one stride behind the huge black head, I motioned for Sarah to stand aside and watch. As soon as she was out of the way I swung with all my strength and hammered my open palm against the back of the mouse's skull.

WHAM! And again, *THUMP!*

'Hey motherfuck!' I screamed, 'What's it like inside that mouse head?'

The enormous mouse scrambled to keep his balance, then wheeled around toward me, panic in his high-pitched squeak: 'Hey! What the heck?'

This time I really leaned into the little fucker, swung sidearm and hammered him so hard that his skull dented in just below the ear.

By now the crowd around us was scattering, moms and dads shrieking instructions as they tried to keep their little ones from getting trampled in the pandemonium. After I'd feinted a couple of jabs and caught the mouse in the abdomen with a solid uppercut he suddenly got deadly serious, squared himself off in front of me, hunkering low with his dukes up in a childish boxer's pose. When I missed with a wild round-house right the big mouse tried to kick me in the nuts but I caught his boot and held on, levering him up and down until he lost his balance and toppled backward to the pavement. I followed him down, scoring heavily to the body with both hands. For a moment we rolled around on the boiling pavement, then I got on top of him and pinned his arms down with my knees. For a moment I paused, surveyed the surrounding crowd like a professional wrestler, arrogantly daring anyone to intercede before I applied my patented finishing hold to their hometown hero. Then, savagely, I slammed my full weight down stiff-armed and locked my hands around the big mouse's throat in a deadly serious choke hold. A tiny gurgling noise came from somewhere deep inside the enormous head and the mouse's body bucked wildly beneath me – it was like riding a brahma bull! By now the crowd that encircled our struggle was near open hysteria, the children wailing and sobbing while their parents tried to shield them from the violence. I tightened my grip around the big mouse's throat and his body movements became even more epileptic – peaked, and then slowly began to subside. I tightened my grip, tightened it more, until the inner energy of my entire being was flowing through my hands and only the big mouse's legs moved, a faltering fibrillation. Oh, the crystal intoxication of that moment! The raw thrust of my vision! My eyes found Sarah in the crowd. She was absolutely beside herself with laughter, tears streaming down her cheeks. In fact, she was drawing almost as much attention from the crowd as I was, laughing hysterically while she shrieked: 'Go for it! Go for it, Shithead! Finish him! Finish the little fucker!'

A couple of fathers edged forward to take limp-wristed swipes at me but I ducked low and maintained my ferocious grip on the big mouse's throat. I didn't see the boot that caught me on the side of the head until a moment too late.

Laughter at Dawn

Instant Changes

Lord only knows how I got into that situation, barely thirty-five and forced to put together a fast six thousand bucks – or I was in *deep* shit with the tax people. A small, one-time-only bequest from my godfather's estate had somehow radically changed my status and, like a gilled creature suddenly summoned by evolution, I found myself on dry land facing a new species of predator – a government computer that wrote nasty form letters.

After coming to terms with the reality of it for a few days the first person I called was my friend D'arcy Hodges in California. D'arcy had been in L.A. doctoring film scripts for five years and he had good connections with all the big studios. More important, D'arcy understood that I liked to think of myself as 'a serious writer' and we related well on that basis. D'arcy had percolated through similar desires himself, having published two rather good experimental novels before heading south to sip the Hollywood nectar.

After tangling with a couple of answering services I finally caught up with D'arcy at his secret number, a Topanga Canyon retreat. Without much explanation he immediately understood the circumstances of the weirdly inverted debtor's prison I'd entered. Sure, he said, no probs. Things were really hopping and he had more work than he could handle. As long as I could get myself down to Hollywood right away there'd be plenty of scripts to work on – in a month I'd make more than enough dough to cover my tax bill.

Six thousand bucks in a month? Carumba! I hadn't made that much dough from my writing in the previous ten years! And I

didn't even have a screen credit! I hung up the telephone and giggled with relief.

Of course, I was prepared for it to be another world down there. Take D'arcy's life, for example. The way I understood it, his writing routine, and reputation, revolved around eleventh-hour deadlocks that came up when the studio brass got nervous about a certain character or plot connection and demanded instant changes. In that situation the studios called on D'arcy, or someone like him, to come in and turn things around with a fast cosmetic rewrite.

When D'arcy described these emergency episodes to me I invariably imagined the scene in terms of stock footage – D'arcy, shouldering into the flooded engine room of a recently torpedoed movie to try and get the bilge pumps working, William Holden shouting down the pipe from the bridge: 'Never mind getting her to float! Just make sure that when she goes down in the last reel the audience understands that the Male Lead is remembering that suitcase full of ransom money we want you to insert in Scene 17b – and maybe a great moment from the hunting trip with his dad in Scene 4. And *happy*, understood?'

'Got it!' D'arcy would bark, duck-diving under the oily prose for thirty-six hours of breathless typing. Scything down people and situations to make room for the ransom money that would ultimately locate the flashback when the ship stood on its nose so the movie could vanish under violin waves.

According to D'arcy, the complicated pressures and problems surrounding these screen-writing assignments were fascinating for him no matter what the movie was about. In fact, he readily admitted without a shred of regret that the specifics of the stories he doctored made no difference to him – it was the underlying complex of mercantile greed and raw ego ambition that gave his profession its vitality and meaning. Naturally, I found this bald admission of compromise appalling and told D'arcy so whenever I got the chance. He was especially vulnerable when he made his

annual trip back up to Canada. For weeks on end he'd do nothing but get drunk enough to tell his old friends that he couldn't understand why he was so fucking unhappy.

'But there aren't any *little* stories left!' he'd bellow when I cornered him. 'Only one big story cloned from all the little stories about all the other stories we already know. People are too quick now, too restless. They can't concentrate on *anything* for more than ninety seconds for crissakes!'

'But what about the concerns of language,' I'd counter, playing, as usual, the serious grad student. 'Where does the problem of consciousness come into your system?'

'A small but alert audience,' he'd jibe, 'and I want you to *promise* that you'll look after all twelve of them for me!'

It'd always been like that with D'arcy and me, playfully unforgiving about the intractable separateness of our viewpoints. In part, I think that accounted for the eerie feeling I'd had after calling him out of the blue to ask for help with my tax problems. I was about to do precisely what D'arcy had done five years before when alimony had forced him to call on an old mutual friend of ours who'd gone to California to earn upkeep for *his* alimony years before that. A daisy-chain of foundering writers who lived on the promise that more money would some day mean more time. Now I was falling into the same trap, harbouring exactly the same misgivings. Needless to say, I felt threatened and frightened in the wake of that phone call.

Over the weekend before my Monday morning departure I did nothing but work on the draft of my new writing, stroking and polishing all day Saturday, then starting a new chapter on Sunday, pushing the story out a couple of pages to a place where it could simmer while I was away in Los Angeles.

It was snowing like hell when I woke up Monday morning. Before I left my apartment I put a clean sheet of paper in the typewriter and propped an unopened package of matches in the

CAUTION

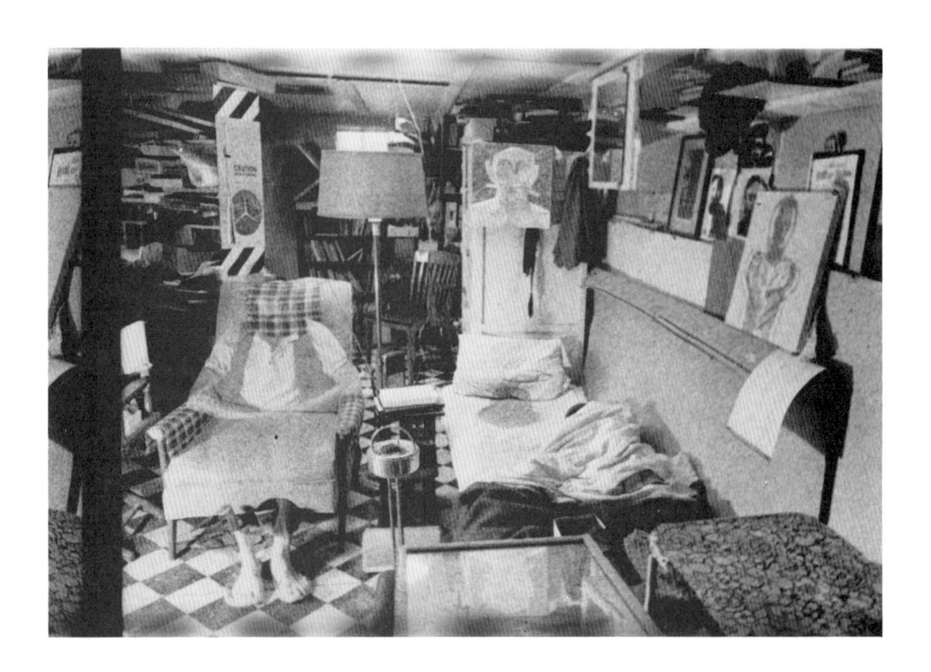
CAUTION

ashtray beside it, hotel room style, reminding myself that it'd feel great to arrive back home in two weeks, maybe with a healthy sunburn, and get down to the serious stuff without that bloody tax bill hanging over my head. Not surprisingly, I'd given absolutely no thought to what I might be called upon to do during my brief stay in Los Angeles. As I say, I'd never in my life tried to write a film script.

Nana Mouskouri

The D'arcy Hodges who met me at the airport was a little thicker around the waist, growing his beard back, but otherwise unchanged from the D'arcy Hodges I'd seen eight months before in Toronto. After happy hugs of greeting he carried my knapsack out to his open Jeep for the drive up into the hills beyond the sprawl of the city. It was cloudless, mid-eighties weather – apparently the first break they'd had after two solid weeks of rain. As we tacked across the grid of freeways I gratefully stripped off my shirt so the hot wind could race over my pale Canadian flesh. D'arcy talked quickly as he drove, obviously excited to have me on his home turf for a change. There were dozens of incredible people I had to meet, a smorgasbord of gala premiers to attend, oceans, mountains and plateaus we might gaze upon if the clear weather held – but first we should drop by to see a producer friend of his who apparently 'had something for me.'

'Just like that?'

'Yup, just like that.'

I fiddled with the strange babble on the AM radio, the way I always do in an unfamiliar place, shouted over the hot racing wind: 'What kind of movies does this guy do?'

'It's a *she*,' he shouted back. 'Ever run across a film called *Harpoon*?' I shook my head. 'No matter – low-budget Melville remake – anyway, this lady's a full-fledged independent now and she's got a

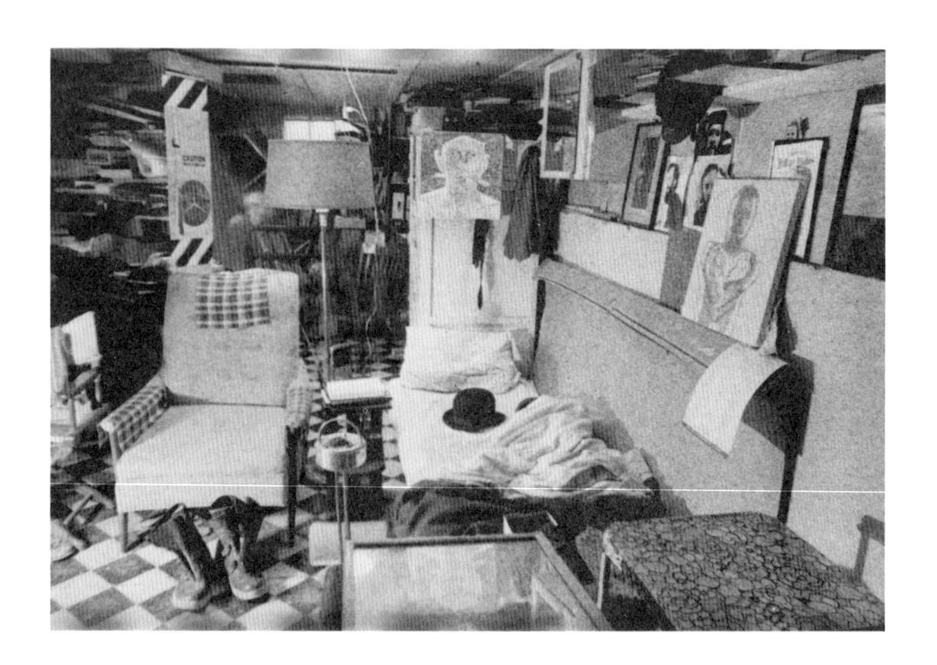

three-picture deal with Universal. They've just handed over the first production property – she says it needs a little nose-job, nothing major – '

God the wind was warm! 'Like what?' I asked, 'What's the story about?'

'No idea!' D'arcy answered, looking over his shoulder as we barged diagonally across four lanes of traffic. 'All she said was the studio guy doesn't think there's enough action. It's not exactly an action picture but they want it to play the fifteen-to-twenty-five bracket – '

I nodded as if that made sense and didn't ask any more questions as we exited off the freeway and started picking our way along one of those traffic clogged semi-suburban/semi-downtown drags that Southern California is so famous for. When D'arcy pulled over and jerked to a stop in front of Eno's House of Beauty I didn't realize that we'd arrived until D'arcy was halfway across the parking lot.

'Her office is upstairs in the back.'

I pulled my shirt on and followed him through a side door, up a flight of stairs and down a dim hallway. There was no sound back there except the steady clack of a manual typewriter.

On entering a small, bright sunroom at the rear of the building we were immediately greeted by a petite woman wearing black horn-rims who rose from behind a desk opposite the door. At first glance she looked almost exactly like Nana Mouskouri. D'arcy introduced the woman as Sarah Duke and we shook hands vigorously. She asked me a couple of quick superficial questions about the flight, the weather in Canada and I told her briefly, Sure, nice flight. Yup, still snowing up there. Just great, she said, Really great. Has D'arcy told you anything about *Laughter at Dawn*?

'No,' I said, turning to D'Arcy for help, 'I thought he slept in.'

'That's funny,' the young woman said, her smile evaporating as she tapped a black binder on her desk for emphasis. '*Laughter at Dawn* is the property we've got for you to work on – '

'Oh, I've heard a bit about it,' I lied, bending to pat an emaciated Afghan with a bald patch near its tail that tiptoed from behind her desk to nose at the crotch of my jeans. After I'd stroked the dog's head a couple of times he shied back and turned slightly aside, released a kind of guttural burp and moved his lips up and down as if something was stuck between his teeth.

'That's the one and only Julius,' Sarah beamed, 'and he's got a bit of a tummyache, don't we Mister Caesar? Don't we Mister Funny Face?'

She scratched the dog's ear and it slunk back to safety behind her desk.

'Shall we talk first or do you want me to read it?' I asked.

'I don't think there's much to talk about, it's only a million-two and the studio's made that back on the television sale. It's a marketing concept, actually – advertisers in up front – so your contract is guaranteed even if the studio doesn't like the rewrite. Four thousand in three steps sound fair?'

I didn't even blink. 'Yeah, that makes sense.'

'*Terrific.* I might as well be straight with you, okay? My situation is this – I'm doing *Laughter at Dawn* as a quid pro quo for Universal. It's their project – if I bring it in on time and under budget they're going to finance this other script that's real important to me – '

'Sarah's got a PhD in Latin American Studies,' D'arcy interjected, as if that explained everything.

'I see,' I said. 'So you really just want to get this one out of the way.'

'You got it.' she laughed. 'Not only that – I wanna *bury* it!'

Now all of us laughed.

'Which isn't to say it's not reasonably good,' she added hastily. 'In fact, it's a fairly interesting story, only it's not – '

'*Your* story?' I suggested.

Sarah smiled, then to D'arcy, 'You were right about this guy, very *sympatico*!'

'Shhh!' D'arcy cautioned, 'You might scare him off.'

All of us laughed again, full and open this time.

'Okay. So where do I go from here?'

Sarah hefted the black binder and held it out to me. 'The first thing you do is give this a read – it's what we've got for a shooting script – and while you're reading see if you can pinpoint why the producer thinks the male lead is ambiguous,' she tapped the binder for emphasis with a long red fingernail, 'I know why *I* think he's ambiguous but it's not the same reason why *they* think he's ambiguous. Anyway, he *is* ambiguous and he has to stay *slightly* ambiguous or the thing won't work. The only question is *how much* ambiguity, and *where*. Don't worry, you'll see what I'm talking about after you've walked through it. Is Wednesday too early to talk?'

'What's today, Monday? Sure, let's make it Wednesday. Shall I call Tuesday to firm up a time?'

'Perfect,' she said, squeezing my hand, 'I'm really looking forward to working with you. Your friend D'arcy here did quite a selling job – '

We smiled and backed away from each other, D'arcy promising to call Sarah soon for that racquetball rematch they'd been threatening to play for months.

As soon as we were back in the Jeep D'arcy let out a little yelp and bounced up and down on his seat. 'What a walk!' he exclaimed, 'I had no idea you'd come on so *supple* – she didn't even ask if you had any credits!'

'I know,' I said, 'Lucky thing too – you know how I feel about falsehood – '

'Oh yeah!' D'arcy said, 'I almost forgot, you're a Canadian!'

We must have laughed for five minutes.

Donna Reed

D'arcy's place up in Topanga Canyon was one of those cantilevered, open plan affairs with picture windows everywhere that *Life Magazine* used to feature in its Modern Living section. The original owner had been Helmut Schmitt, a legendary cameraman of the old school who'd accumulated a handsome bankroll shooting quickies for Sam Wacker. Subsequently the house had changed hands a couple of times – now D'arcy was renting it from Billy Reed, one of Donna Reed's kids, who'd drifted off to Goa a few years before.

Coming from my humble surroundings D'arcy's place was a rich Technicolour fantasy. With a little difficulty I reined in the ga-ga reaction, not wanting to seem too much the hick on my first day in town. Look straight down into a real canyon while you have a crap? So what?

As soon as he'd shown me around and settled my stuff in the guest room D'arcy said he had to dash off for the rest of the day, his new girl friend was moving out on her husband. D'arcy had promised to help hump her cartons over to a pal's place in Venice. He'd try to get back sometime in the early evening. I said that plan was absolutely no problem for me, he should let the move take as long as it took, I'd make myself comfortable and try to get something going with Sarah's script.

The Real

After D'arcy left I poked around his place, seeing, through the lens of accumulated objects, who he actually was, or rather, who he'd become since we'd lived a half-block from each other in the west end of Toronto. The expensive Scandinavian furniture had obviously come with the place, so I discounted it, concentrating instead on the personal bric-à-brac D'arcy had crammed into his study – a

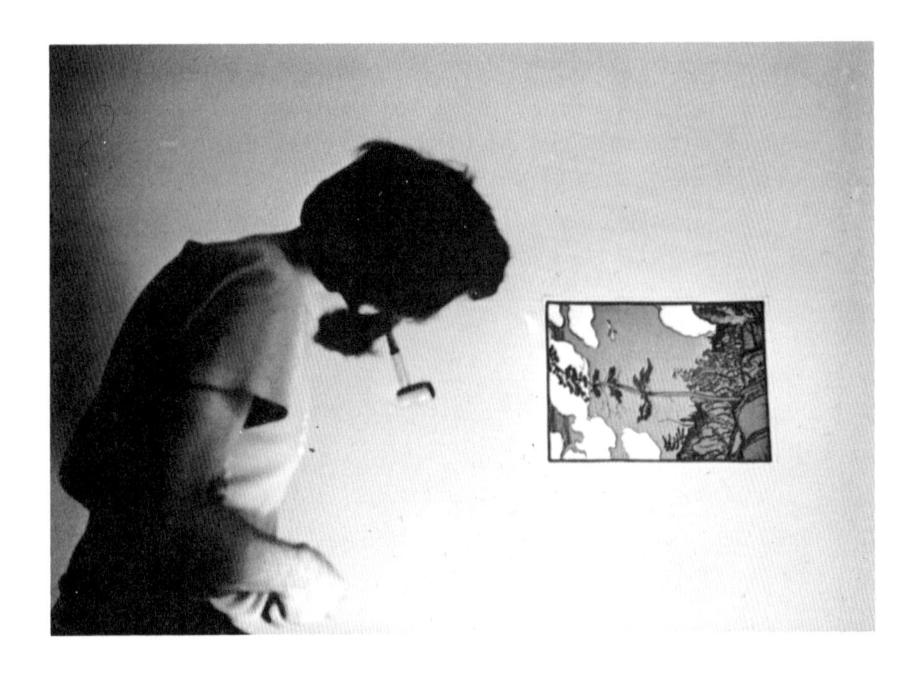

rickety little shed some crazed Sunday carpenter had added on under the main platform of the house by tacking old window frames and junk lumber to the redwood timbers. What a strange assortment of books! The complete works of HD, Joyce and Hammett on a top shelf, a dozen volumes of Zen commentary, another dozen about ancient Egypt, then rows and rows of cheap dime store novels ending with a bottom shelf of scripts and technical books about film-making. I took one of the Egyptian books down and opened it, the glue in the binding cracked sharply, a cash register slip lay flat inside the front cover. Then there was the framed stuff on the walls, aside from a few kitschy movie posters from the 50s, the rest, floor to ceiling, consisted of photographs, many inscribed as mementoes by probably well-known people whose faces and signatures I didn't recognize. The collection of photographs was unified by the omnipresently candid smile on D'arcy's face in the foreground grouping. An odd *Kilroy was here* motif began to emerge as I moved from one photograph to the next. D'arcy proclaiming his dark tan and white white teeth with devilish abandon in frame after frame. As I scanned the images the panorama of D'arcy's new life made no secure connection with the person I'd known – the quiet guy down the street who was interested in astronomy, horticulture (his backyard thick with wild irises) and the compositional techniques of Kurt Schwitters.

A small desk stood square in the centre of D'arcy's study, the surface buried under a good foot of paper – dog-eared scripts, unpaid bills, receipts from fancy restaurants, press releases, magazine and newspaper clippings, unopened correspondence and – in the centre of it all – an unwieldy stack of yellow legal-length paper covered with cramped scrawl. I leafed through a section of the manuscript but couldn't decipher anything except the odd exchange of dialogue where D'arcy's pen had slowed down enough to form the letters properly, and the typed title page:

OUTLINE FOR M. HIRSH

SC. 19-22

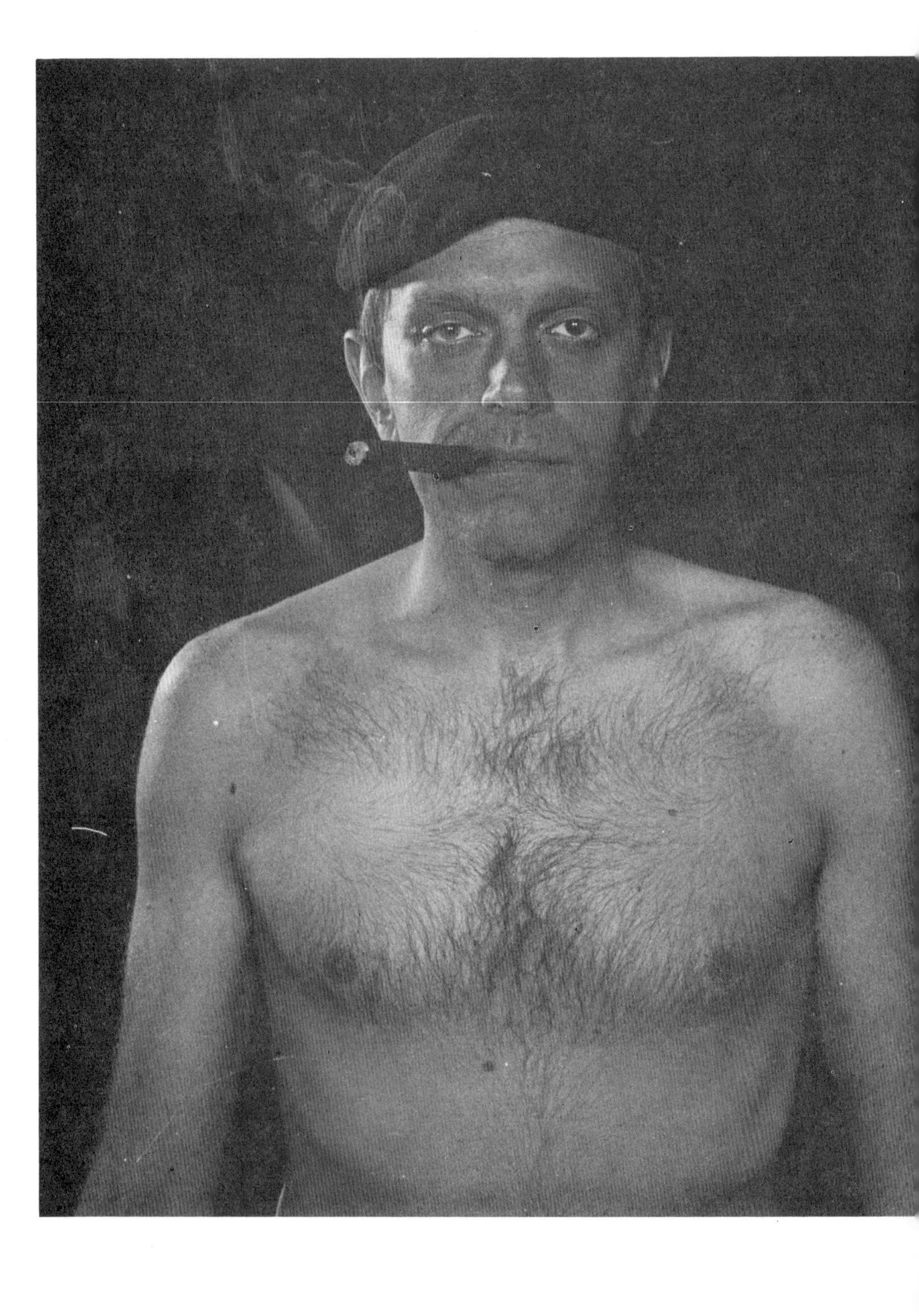

I restacked the scrambled pages as best I could and put them on the top of the surrounding pile so the crater at the centre of the desk would be clear, then went upstairs, picked up a cold beer and my copy of *Laughter at Dawn,* and came back down to set to work.

The Basic Storyline

Laughter at Dawn was short, about ninety pages, and I finished my first reading in less than an hour, only breaking concentration to fetch more beer. The basic storyline had to do with a gaggle of stock characters who hustled together in an old-style carnival – one of those anachronistic Lions Club operations you see in the parking lots of suburban shopping malls. The script's setting and atmosphere weren't bad in and of themselves – with that cast of snake oil salesmen the story could conceivably have generated an interesting aura of doomed Willie Loman obsolescence. It could have gone that way, but it didn't, because the hack who'd written the first draft had stuck this two-dimensional 'hero' in the foreground, an Ivy League kid gone wrong named David Phipps. According to the script Phipps had tried to outdistance his materially secure background (dad an advertising man) by hiring on as the Crown & Anchor man with the band of stereotyped gypsies who ran the carnival. Then, about page forty, the kid fell in love with a vacant-eyed vagabond girl. For awhile the two of them could hardly believe that they were actually helping each other cut through the existential guck. The story rounded another corner and it turned out the vagabond girl had a rare bone disease. First Rule of Screenwriting, I thought to myself, when in doubt go for bone disease. For the next dozen scenes David Phipps tried to decide whether or not he should ask his wealthy father to pay for the girl's chemotherapy. Meanwhile in the background a couple of sub-plots spun and fizzled like cheap fireworks in the rain. In the end it turned out the kid had his share of stubborn pride. His dad had always used

money to manipulate him. Carnival life had made him free and honest for the first time. In the last scene Phipps, standing fast against compromise, decided not to accept his father's financial assistance. The vagabond girl, doomed now to an early grave, realized that her love had helped Phipps make the most important decision in his life. Without warning she vanished into the night leaving behind a note and a wild rose. I don't need to tell you what the note said – you'll find it somewhere between pages 19 and 36 of your TV Guide.

But, then again – sure, why not? There was no reason for that causality to fail providing the mixed-up kid named David Phipps was played by the young Monty Clift. But for the budget Sarah Duke was talking it was clear the male lead would probably be some dickhead who looked good in Levis and knew enough about acting to shuffle across a sound stage and stop on a piece of masking tape. On page after page of the script somebody had scrawled bold advice across Phipps' speeches with a thick red magic marker, like: *Not confused enough,* or *Show don't tell*! or *What's he thinking*!! Pages 78 and 79 were stroked out completely by the angry red felt pen, which then scrawled:

I've GOTTA care about DAD! Put him together with OLD INDIAN on midway?

I looked out the window, followed the twist of the road along the floor of the canyon. Use the old Indian on the midway? Jesus – this was going to be discouraging. Something like a cuckoo clock chimed upstairs, no, more rhythmic, a glockenspiel repeating a snatch of some tune – *Me & My Shadow*? – over and over again. The doorbell! I tossed the script aside and trotted upstairs.

Tim Considine

By the time I made it to the front door, the bell ringer was rapping hard with an urgent knuckle. I pulled the door wide open, confronted a young kid with a brush cut dressed in olive drab battle fatigues.

'S'cuse me, sir, I'm with the 101st Airborne Reserves – the Big Red One? Are you the occupant here?' The kid delivered his speech with a cheerful yet automatic tone. It occured to me that he looked a bit like Tim Considine from the old *Spin & Marty* television series.

'Not really,' I said, 'I'm visiting from Canada, what's the – '

Interrupting apologetically: 'Well, we're sorry to bother you, sir, but we're putting the entire Upper Trail area on slide alert. All that rain last weekend opened up a couple of cracks yea-big on the ridge. There's a team from Cal Tech up there evaluating it so there's no real cause for alarm. We'll let you know in plenty of time if the authorities issue an evacuation order, okay?' A walkie-talkie squawked disjointed coordinates at the kid's hip and he fumbled awkwardly to click it off, smiling to me, a little embarrassed.

'Like fuckin' Eagle Scouts,' he said.

'I bet,' I said, 'listen, I'm new here – what are the odds of a slide? Should I have my stuff packed?'

'I'd say the odds would be something like, oh ... eighty-twenty.'

'Eighty-twenty? Which way?'

'I keep forgetting you aren't from around here,' the kid paused, bemused. 'Well, there actually isn't much danger. My reserve unit comes up the canyons on these manoeuvres practically every time it rains – like to keep us busy, yunno – where you from in Canada?'

'Toronto,' I said. 'Heard of it?'

'T.O! 'Course I've heard of it!' the kid bubbled. 'Would you believe I'm from Red Lake?'

Red Lake!

'Not the Red Lake up near Kenora?'

'Yup, a shade over three hundred clicks into the bush from there. I been down here nearly four years trying to break in as an actor – '

'Well, I'll be damned!' I said, examining the kid in a fresh light. 'An actor, eh?'

'Yup, finally got one of the good agents going for me last spring. He's landed me a supporting role in a half-hour pilot, walk-on parts in a few features, lots of ads – '

'Wait a minute,' I said, finally catching the glimpse, 'I think I saw, aren't you. . . razor blades? No, you're – '

'Right on, brother!' the kid laughed heartily. 'You mean my Gillette Foamy – that one's been paying the rent for six months!'

'*Amazing!*' I said, truly amazed. 'I mean, right away I *knew* I recognized that face.' I pointed to his face as if both of us were looking at it.

'I guess a lot of people recognize it by now.' The kid showed me a gleaming set of ultra-straight teeth. 'Anyway, listen I gotta run, I have to make a checkpoint two miles down the road or our unit will get penalized. Maybe I'll have time to stop by for a chat on my way back up – '

'Sure thing,' I said. 'Lots of beer in the fridge.'

'Sounds *good!*' the kid said happily, then turned to jog off up the driveway, steadying the swing of the walkie-talkie at his hip with one hand.

A Fold in the Curtain

Back inside I opened another can of Coors and flipped through D'arcy's record collection until I found something interesting to put on – the Westminster Boys' Choir doing liturgical works by Handel – that old 'Pre-puberty Sound.' I stretched out in the hammock that hung across one end of the main upstairs room and closed my eyes to listen. It was a superb recording, the clean,

solemn voices of the little boys matched meticulously for grain, the precise mix reverberating upward, I imagined, toward a damp stone ceiling somewhere high in the Italian Alps. I swung the hammock with my foot and let the voices penetrate to my soft spot, relaxed in the mood of quietly depersonalized romanticism air travel always engendered in me.

And maybe a mud slide, I thought to myself. Sure thing. *Perfect.*

As my eye muscles relaxed I let them toy with the perceptual trick I'd learned as a child – projecting in-bent images of the room on the back of my eyelids, a kind of fish-eye/ wrong-end-of-the-telescope distortion that only exhaustion could induce. I let my mind fragment – thought about the empty sheet of white paper in my typewriter back in Toronto. The unopened package of matches in the clean ashtray beside it. I let the two rooms, the one I was in and the one where I'd been, drift together and merge in semi-consciousness. Thought about the hanging folds of my winter coat on the back of the hall door, enumerated the contents of all the pockets. The dripping bathroom faucet down the hall. The things I could never change across a three-hour time difference. I remembered the man who'd sat beside me on the plane from Chicago, a professor from Johns Hopkins with psoriasis flakes in his eyebrows winging south for a linguistics conference at UCLA. He hadn't talked to me much except to say that the last linguistics conference had been in Brasilia. The professor drank gin and tonic, read Flann O'Brien's *At Swim-Two-Birds*. Emerald green end-papers. Probably still within a hundred miles of me ... I let my eyes work their trick and envisioned what he was doing – exchanging shop-talk with a colleague, long-separated friends, the two of them sipping chilled domestic rosé on a patio overhung with wisteria. Wagon trains drawing up in a circle between the towering mountains of the dead and the green foothills of the as yet unborn. The boys' choir again, the voices hushed and secret in their suggestion of larger ideas – the blue vein of an iris petal in close-up anchoring the eye before it moves up and out across the full panorama of the garden. Ambiguous kid downstairs named David Phipps, I was wasting his oxygen – think about it right or get depressed. Don't know the first thing about screenplays. Five thousand miles away an axe buried in the keyboard of my typewriter. Three hundred beyond that a vast National Revenue computer. Preaddressed envelopes conjured electrically. A bald civil servant stacking them into straight packets, putting elastic bands around each packet, the packets into canvas bags full of other packets. He drags the canvas bags into a corridor by anonymous elevators. Record needle bumps, steady dull rhythm pushing me further into sleep. A Japanese pond, a clump of blue irises ...

a fold in the curtain ...

Bamma-BAMMA-*Bamma*!

'Wh-what?'

I tumbled out of the hammock, lurched across the room. The front door again.

Red Lake Density

The Gillette Foamy Reservist greeted me with a warm, familiar smile.

'Hi there,' I said, rubbing my eyes groggily, 'I was sleeping off the jet lag. Want to come in for a minute?'

'You bet,' the kid clicked off his walkie-talkie and stepped inside, 'My unit doesn't have to be back on the truck for forty-five minutes – hey, this is quite the spot.'

I was in the kitchen fetching a couple of cold beers: 'Ever get back to Red Lake?' I handed the kid his bottle across the red formica counter and came around to join him.

'Sure, I was back up to see my folks two Christmases ago, had to go, my twin brother's restaurant went bankrupt and – '

'Oh-oh, I think I already know this story,' I said as we took our places on the generous throw cushions D'arcy had piled into the corner where the picture windows joined their views of the canyon.

'Yeah, pretty sad actually.' The kid rolled the can between his hands, serious and preoccupied. 'Dave and I were close – you can imagine how it is with identical twins. He had this crazy notion that you could make money running a fancy restaurant in Red Lake – that all the guys from the pulp mill would come there to eat if it was one price for everything off a buffet – you know, surf 'n' turf – all that crap.' The kid shook a Camel loose from his pack and lit it carefully. I realized that under that tan he was probably a few years older than I'd thought, maybe late-twenties.

'And so?' I said, waiting for the punchline, 'What went wrong?'

The kid looked out the window and drew in smoke. 'Bastards up there dropped on him like vultures – my old man was with management at Kimberley-Clark and there was always this resentment – so every night the bohunks showed up at Dave's place for a big feed after they got off shift. It got to be a big game for them to pig out as much as they could on the buffet, then go downstairs and puke on the floor, wipe their asses on the roller towels and stagger back up to start all over again. When they were good and drunk they'd pick fights with each other, break the place up pretty good until the Mounties arrived. It was like they were making my brother pay for everything they hated about their lives up there.'

'That's so sad it's funny,' I said, trying not to laugh. 'I mean, it's so so *Canadian*. Fucking lobster tails and Muzak in Red Lake! *WOW* –' I was laughing despite myself. 'But I know it's not that funny, I mean, the restaurant goes belly up and your poor brother has to –'

'He put a shotgun in his mouth.'

The kid kept his eyes out the window and sipped beer.

'Jesus,' I whispered, 'Listen, I'm really sorry. I had no idea. I thought you were – '

'Don't apologize, *please*.' the Gillette kid gave me a sad grin. 'It *is* funny, dammit. The guys who decide to stay up there just keep

working on it and working on it until it happens – a car, a hunting accident, a fight over some squaw in the local draught room – you know what it's like in the bush.'

'I sure do,' I said glumly.

We left a little window of silence so the unpleasant topic could find its own way out.

'I guess you'd be down here on a winter holiday, then – ' the kid suggested finally.

'Working holiday. I'm rewriting a film script.'

'Oh yeah?' The kid's face lit up. 'Feature?'

'Uh-huh, I've only read it over once but it seems – ' the doorbell rang again and I excused myself in mid-sentence, trotted across the room. A young woman greeted me this time. She was tiny, less than five feet tall, barefoot, wearing cut-off denims. Her hair was short, blonde with black roots.

'Hi!' the tiny woman peeped with a Texas twang, 'I'm Linda-Jo Peters from up on the hill, is D'arcy here?'

'No, I'm afraid he's – '

'Hi-ya Linda-Jo!' the kid hollered from behind me.

Linda-Jo shaded her eyes with one hand and peered into the room, yelped:

'Eh-meel? I thought you was s'posed to be on yer exercises – '

'Care for a beer?' I asked.

'That'd be *awful* nice,' she said, skipping into the room, 'Only reason I actually come over was to tell D'arcy I got some his mail by accident.' She exchanged a couple of envelopes for the beer I offered and we went across the room to the cushions under the window. To my surprise the girl named Linda-Jo Peters plumped herself down directly on top of the kid named Emile and bounced up and down, giggling.

'We so blessed *lucky* to have this boy protecting us from this here *slahd*,' squirming like a little girl on her father's knee until the kid managed to tickle her off to one side.

'I take it you two know each other,' I said, sitting down on the cushions opposite them.

'Linda-Jo? You bet – ' Emile poked her in the ribs, 'Linda-Jo's kind of a mascot for my Reserve Unit. Yunno, she's – '

'Eh-*meel*, you stop! Don't you *dare*!'

'C'mon Lindy, this guy's from Canada, he'll understand.'

'I mean it, 'Meel! You say so much as *one* more – '

The telephone rang and I excused myself as the two of them started to wrestle again, Linda-Jo squealing hysterically as the kid named Emile gained control, mounted her and pinned her arms down with his knees.

In the kitchen I got myself a fresh beer and picked up the phone on the fourth ring. When I told the caller, a Mr Hirsch, that D'arcy wasn't home, he got very belligerent, snarling a string of brusque questions at me about Who was I? and What was I doing in *that* house? as if I was some kind of enemy saboteur. Before he hung up Mr Hirsch made me take down four separate phone numbers and check the digits back to him. He said I was to be *sure* D'arcy called back, no matter what time he got home. As I hung up the receiver it occurred to me that anyone as rude and demanding as Mr Hirsch had to be extremely powerful.

As I re-entered the main room, Emile and Linda-Jo Peters were halfway to the front door.

'You guys have to go?' I asked, a little fuddled by the abrupt change of venue.

'I got *paaahs* in the oven next door,' Linda-Jo drawled. 'And if Emile don't make his deadline back at that truck his whole Unit'll get *peen*-lized, won't it Eh-meel?'

'Thanks a lot for the beer,' Emile said, shaking my hand. 'I'm sure we'll see each other again. If it keeps raining.'

'Hope so,' I said. 'I'll probably see you anyway – with Gillette Foamy all over your face.'

'Well, here's hoping,' Emile chirped, pumping my hand eagerly as

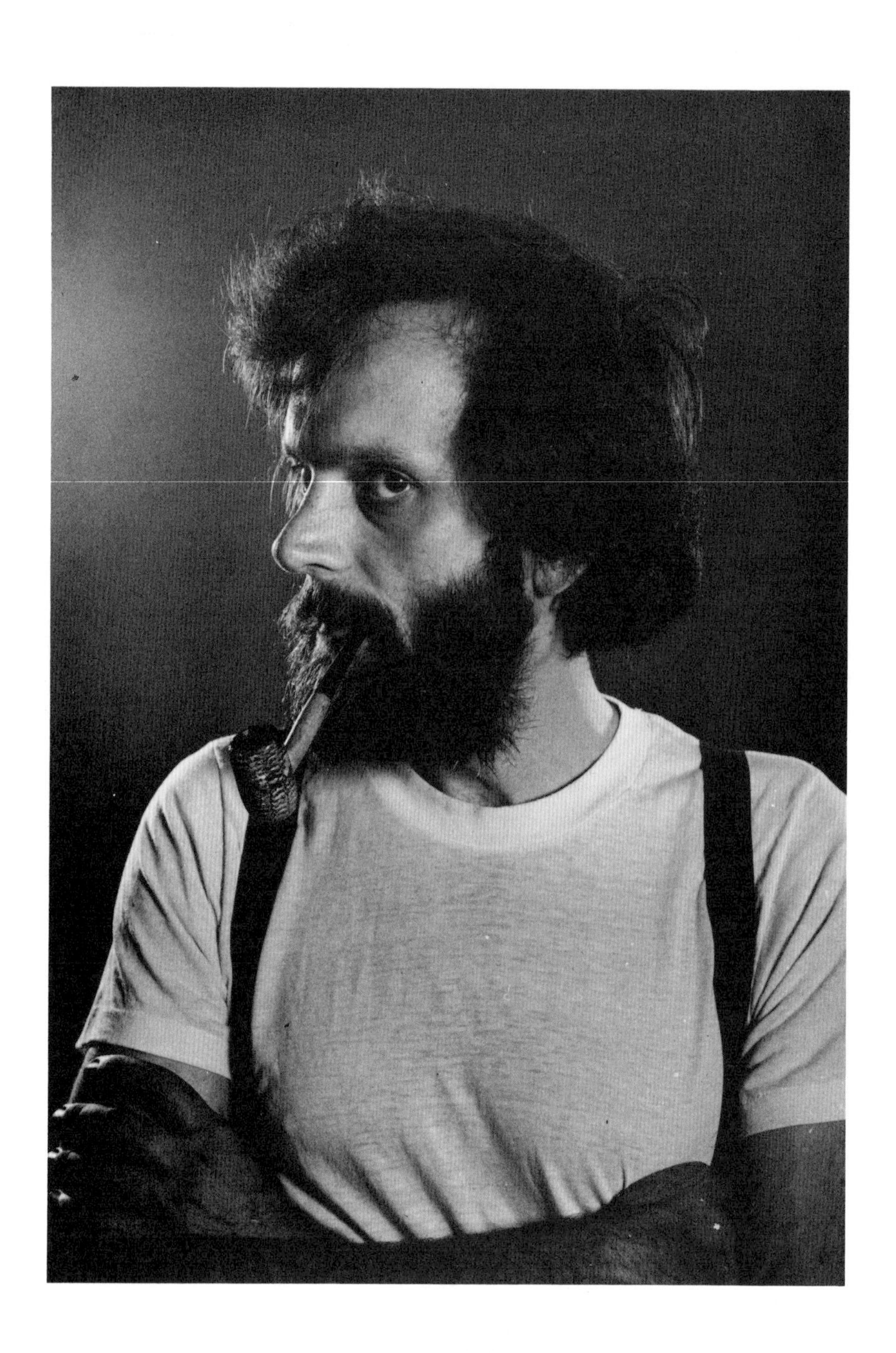

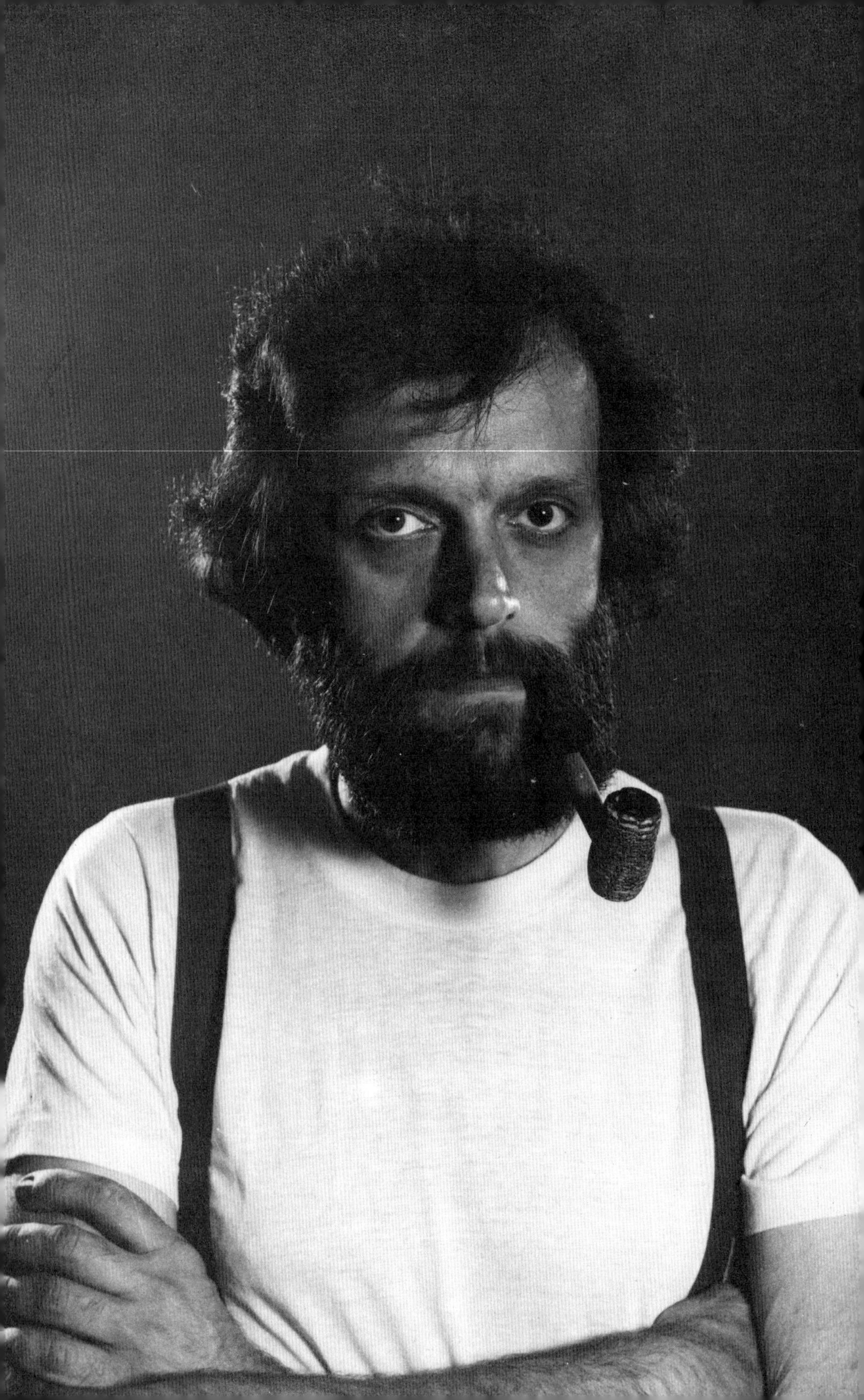

he followed Linda-Jo Peters out the door. 'Good luck with your script!'

'Thanks!'

Snap, Crackle & Pop

I went to the kitchen window and watched the two of them stroll up and across the driveway. Halfway up the slope Emile grabbed ahold of Linda-Jo Peters' rear end with one hand and she whirled around shrieking with girlish laughter, swatted him on the side of the head, then broke loose and scampered away, disappearing around the corner of the boxwood hedge with her young soldier boy calling out threats as he struggled to catch up.

The late afternoon sunlight had dulled, as if a storm was gathering. I drank another can of beer, then went outside to watch as dark thunderheads lumbered into place – heat lightning booming, the sound of flexing sheet metal somewhere on the far side of the ridge. Twenty minutes later the clouds began to spit fat bullets of hot rain and twenty minutes after that it was coming straight down, a dense, undulating curtain – like the machine rain in that old Gene Kelly movie. I went back to my room and lay down for a nap, dodging and riding in the narrowing space between thunder and lightning as I let the time difference take over again.

Hours folded into themselves, disappeared down a hole.

I awoke, startled by the thump of a car door, the rattle of a key in the lock.

The room was black dark, rain still tapped lightly on the skylight above my bed. My watch said ten but I couldn't remember whether or not I'd set it back on the plane.

The front door slammed shut, and a light came on in the main room at the far end of the hall. I called out D'arcy's name and he answered, clumped down the hall to meet me in the doorway. His face was drawn and grim in the dim light, as if he faltered on the brink of some penetrating fatigue. Still half-asleep, I started to jokingly recount how I'd occupied my first day in sunny Southern California but D'arcy's solemn face didn't register a response, it was as though he couldn't concentrate enough to laugh. When I asked him if something had gone wrong that afternoon he immediately perked up, said: No, nothing like that. It was just all the packing and unpacking of cartons. He was bushed.

We went back down the hall into the main room and I got a couple of beers from the kitchen. Remembering Hirsch's phone call I started to recount his weirdly belligerent message and that's what broke D'arcy wide, wide open.

Without a word of explanation he wheeled around, grabbed the first thing on the counter, an ashtray brimming with cigarette butts, and pitched it against the wall on the opposite side of the living room. Then, shouting a string of filthy epithets, he spun around and booted the front door so hard that something in the kitchen fell off a shelf and shattered in the sink. D'arcy came back into focus and barged past me into the kitchen to see what had broken – a cut-glass vase full of dried flowers. While he cleaned up the mess he tried to tell me what was going on with a trembling angry voice. I switched on the overhead bulb in the kitchen and sat down at the breakfast table to listen.

Apparently D'arcy's current girlfriend's husband, a man named Dean Sharp, was one of the most successful and powerful screenwriters in Hollywood. He was so bankable that instead of paying for scripts the studios gave him chunks of stock. That very afternoon Dean Sharp had returned unexpectedly from a business trip to New York and found D'arcy and the woman, his wife, driving off with a trailer-full of furniture. Sharp immediately flew into a jealous frenzy, threatened both of them physically, even broke a mop handle over the hood of D'arcy's Jeep. When that didn't work

Sharp told him he should expect a call from the head of the studio where he, D'arcy, got most of his film writing assignments. Hirsch, the guy I'd talked to, was the studio wheel's second-in-command. D'arcy had already heard from him. Hirsch told D'arcy to get himself a good lawyer because the studio was tearing up his three-year screenwriting contract.

'They've torn up my fucking contract!' D'arcy shrieked, hurling a handful of broken glass into the garbage pail under the sink. He wheeled around and stabbed a bloody finger at me, still shouting, as he recounted *EXACTLY* what he'd told Hirsch to do the next time he experienced an especially limber moment. I told D'arcy his finger was bleeding and he stuck it in his mouth, continuing his rehearsal of threats while I went down the hall and fumbled around in the unfamiliar bathroom cabinet until I found a Band-aid. The phone in the kitchen rang and I heard D'arcy answer it gruffly, then fall into silence. As I re-entered the kitchen D'arcy started trying to interrupt whoever was on the other end. I unpeeled the band-aid and motioned for him to lift the cut finger that hung at his side, the wound dripping a puddle of dark blood on the linoleum floor. As I applied bandage to finger, D'arcy repeatedly tried to interrupt the person on the other end, demanding that his caller: BE REASONABLE! and STAND UP TO THAT SHIT! – then he abruptly dropped his argument in mid-sentence and plumped the receiver back into its cradle.

He shook his head glumly. It's all fucked up now, he said quietly, That was Sarah Duke. Her too? I asked. Yup, same fuckin' studio. Hirsch was gonna try and cut D'arcy off at the knees. I said that kind of thing never really happened and D'arcy rocked from foot to foot with sinister laughter, sucking his finger as if he'd forgotten that the cut was now bandaged. In this league that kind of thing *always* happened, he said. But it *wasn't* going to happen this time. No way. He'd been working on a fail-safe deal that Hirsch couldn't touch. He was close friends with a stock broker who had direct

access to the A.F. of L. C.I.O. Pension Fund. In six months they'd be packaging their own films. Hirsch could go piss up a rope for all D'arcy cared. He banged open a row of cupboards and rummaged around until he found a fifth of Jack Daniels, took two small tumblers from an adjacent shelf and filled them to the brim. He was laughing crazily now, pontificating about the nature of bad luck as if only a vase full of dried flowers had broken in the sink, waving the bandaged finger like a conductor's baton to command my attention as he came in low to elaborate on the sick hypocrisy of the people you had to work with in this business if you ever wanted to save enough money to get back to serious writing.

We toasted each other and drained our glasses. As the bourbon went down D'arcy slumped a little and said he'd best get to bed right away or he'd likely fall on his face. Apparently some understanding neighbour had given him a strong barbiturate that afternoon after his first telephone battle with Hirsch. D'arcy's eyelids lowered and he staggered a little while he told me not to worry. No sweat-a-rooney. There were a dozen ways we could deal around this shit-storm and land me another writing job to pay the tax bill back in Canada. I told him to forget it, if things didn't materialize I'd slip back across the border and apply for a new social insurance number under an assumed name – maybe I'd use D'arcy Hodges! That really got a good laugh out of him. All the way down the hall. We said goodnight on the ragged tail end of it and closed the doors of our adjoining rooms.

As D'arcy bumped around on the other side of the wall he told me in a thick voice that I had to make sure he got up at five the next morning to do his Tai chi. If he didn't do his Tai chi the whole day would get buggered up.

I said sure-sure-sure and stepped out of my clothes, got into bed, and flipped through a couple of old *National Geographics* from under the night table, getting part way through a story called '*Georgian Bay Wonderland*' before the thrum and putter of a moth against the shade lulled me to sleep.

DEAD END

A little after dawn something startled me and I sat bolt upright semi-conscious, blinking in the pearl grey light until I'd organized the unfamiliar dimensions of the room. Dogs were barking somewhere far below – deep bays and excited yelps. Rain still puttered busily on the skylight. I listened to the dogs, wondering. The glass in the skylight rattled in its frame, buffeted by some phantom wind. Then, a deep grumble. Another, much deeper. D'arcy groaned awake and mumbled something through the thin wall, then:

'What the – !'

I swung my legs over the side of the bed and started to stand up as the floor quivered underfoot, the furniture moving away from me as the room began to shimmy angularly downward with an explosive snap, crackle and pop of rending timbers.

Paradise Lost

A Blurring Blade

Huh?

I opened my eyes, listened up into the cool, dim air – the reassuring thrum of an air conditioner fluttering drapes on the other side of the room, the rolling thunder of combers arriving on a nearby shore. In the open spaces between the waves a tropical warbler cast shrill arcs of melody across what had to be a newly-dawned morning. I didn't know nearly as much as I would in twenty minutes. In the meantime, I knew enough to get started. I was half-awake, naked on a strange bed inside a dim seaside bungalow somewhere on the other side of the world. Phasing in and out, wading upstream against the jet lag, trying to fit it together.

'Last night you came to an island on the other side of the world,' I reminded myself, 'That's Indonesia out there – '

The geographic fact didn't register. The same kind of numb, non-response I'd had the previous evening when we'd flown across the International Dateline – that arbitrary mid-Pacific stroke where the civilized world conveniently changes days, Monday suddenly Sunday, nobody caught awake in the odd jump-cut limbo except me and the Navy guy. I desperately wanted the inside of that Jumbo to crackle with metaphysical *leger de main.* No way. Tomorrow and yesterday were nothing but words, identical caterpillars of sawdust creeping along behind a blurring blade.

And now it was later still and I'd been carried forward yet again. Perhaps, to a modest beach bungalow on the other side of the world. A cheap hotel recommended by my taxi driver. And now my wheels were spinning. Maybe if I tried to reconstruct the Navy guy, tabulated exact details to see if he amounted to anything substantial enough to ground me in my foreign surroundings.

Gee Whiz

The Navy guy who'd been beside me on the Pan Am 747 was, I'd guess, in his late 30s, and *real* fit. The enamelled badge on the breast pocket of his dress whites said: *Lt. David Phipps.* He had closely shaven gun-metal cheeks, a precise crescent moustache, pink, pink fingernails, a trim regulation haircut salt and peppered at the temples. All of that constellated around a physical presence that was otherwise indistinct – one of those grain-fed faces you can't recall in close detail ten minutes after you break visual contact – pleasant, yet totally forgettable, like the host on an afternoon talk show.

Lt. Phipps was a career officer heading back to pick up his submarine in Guam after 3 weeks of R&R with his family in San Diego. Since I was curious about life on board a nuclear submarine and Lt. Phipps clearly wanted to trust me, indeed, seemed to almost *need* my approval, we ended up talking non-stop all the way from San Francisco to Guam. A little under nine hours in the air.

According to Lt. Phipps, after one of his regular stateside sojourns away from the Pacific Fleet the orderly rotation returned him to America's enormous military complex at Guam – B-52s supported by two tactical squadrons of F-14 Tomcats, a crack battalion of combat-hardened Marines and, most important for Lt. Phipps, the second largest submarine pen in the world – only the Soviet installation at Murmansk was bigger.

Arriving back on the island Lt. Phipps would be piped aboard the *Robert E. Lee* a Rickover Class vessel with anti-submarine capabilities. As soon as the crew had reassembled the *Lee* left Guam by night – 'pushed' in Navy parlance – went a couple of miles off shore, blew the tanks, and pitched straight down the wall of a submarine canyon wall into the Mariana Trench – an almost vertical drop-off into 36,000 feet of water. The greatest ocean depth in the world.

For the next six weeks the *Lee* would remain submerged, ghosting back and forth between various 'keyholes' on the Pacific floor. In the centre of each keyhole American military intelligence had installed sophisticated listening devices that recorded and categorized the propeller signatures of Russia's rapidly expanding submarine fleet. According to Lt. Phipps these listening devices were about the size of a boxcar, weighed 40 tons, and cost a shade under twenty million bucks. His job on board the *Lee* was to trigger high density transmission pulses from the listening devices, decode the print-out and boil it down to a one-page summary for the skipper's daily breakfast prep. It was the skipper's job to keep the *Lee* undetected, 'incognito' as they termed it, while trying to tail-gate one of the Russian missile subs that operated in the area. 'Hot pursuit exercises that safeguard the integrity of America's retaliatory capability', as Lt. Phipps termed it.

And you better believe the *Lee* was ready to play hard ball with the bears in Moscow! She was armed with Smart Torpedoes. 'Smart' because they had quartz-based gyros designed by the top defence specialists at GE. Heat sensitive homing video programmed by a legendary boy-genius at RCA. According to Lt. Phipps this was ultra-top-secret stuff. In fact, probably only a hundred guys in the entire world had a precise understanding of what was inside the black boxes on those Smart Torpedoes. And it just so happened I was sitting beside one of them.

Gee, I said, that's really something.

Nah, Lt. Phipps shrugged off a terse little smile. As far as he was concerned it was just nuts and bolts. No big thing, really. Although, if you believed Navy regulations, a guy with his ordinance clearance wasn't even supposed to talk to himself about it. But that was a bunch of donkey doo. Sure, you had to be plenty careful, had to

know what you could and couldn't say – at the same time a guy was entitled to live a normal life, eh? For instance, what about the way we'd ended up sitting next to each other on the plane? Lt. Phipps couldn't sleep on planes and the long leg out to Guam normally bored the pants off him. As it happened, I was sitting in the next seat and he liked talking to me. He knew I was a solid guy. On the same wave length and all that. So what if we tipped back a few beer and shot the breeze? Big deal! No way some Brass Hat was gonna convince him there was anything wrong with that. And if I happened to ask him about the Smart Torpedoes? No-o-o problem, senor. Naturally, there were certain things he could tell me and other things that he wouldn't tell me, *ever.* Even if I branded his nuts with a red-hot coat hanger. If I was interested, Lt. Phipps said he'd show me what he meant. Show me *exactly* where the line was. Lt. Phipps slid a careful hand inside his jacket, and paused, waiting to be coaxed.

Gee, I said, That'd be really interesting – if you're sure you won't get in trouble.

Lt. Phipps drained his Coors, pulled a ballpoint pen from his inside pocket and started sketching a cross-section of the Smart Torpedo on the back of his Pan Am cocktail napkin. As he roughed in schematics for the internal components Lt. Phipps described the inter-related functions of the various sections in surprising detail. As if someday I might want to mock up a Smart Torpedo in my basement shop.

When he got to the nose section of the weapon system, the place where they housed the top-secret black boxes, Lt. Phipps lowered his voice a notch, loosened the motion of his pen to shade in the extent of the off-limits area. Shading over the stuff he'd *never* describe to anyone, even if he was expertly tortured to the doorstep of Hell by the most blood-thirsty lunatics on earth. Having made his point about where the no-talkie line was, I fully expected Lt. Phipps to put his sketch away and change the subject. Strangely, he

didn't. Instead, he kept talking in that low, secret drone – describing in vivid detail the brutally efficient training techniques the Navy used to harden-up officers like him who'd been selected for top secret clearance. There was a special school where they taught you how to withstand all the latest interrogation techniques. Everything from ultra-sonic rumbles that made you shit your pants right up to sophisticated psychological stuff that'd convince a guy his mom was strapped down next door getting it slow and steady from a Doberman. On graduation from the Pentagon's torture school a guy was ready for the dwarfs and hunchbacks. Ready to blow his winger's head off if it came down to the short and curlies.

I did my best to appear interested in this stuff arching my eyebrows in gee whiz astonishment whenever Lt. Phipps monitored my face. In fact, I wasn't all that curious about the pain thresholds that separated me from the secrets inside a Smart Torpedo. What I really wanted to talk about were the meat and potato realities. The day-to-day stuff about what it was like to live inside a metal tube that stayed under water for six weeks at a stretch. For instance, what about whacking off? With seventy healthy young sailors cooped up with no gals there'd have to be a fair amount of the old whacker-oony. Probably *thousands* of solo ejaculations. How would the commanding officers deal with that reality? Openly – special private cubicles set aside with black lights and wall-size posters of Cheryl Tiegs in a wet t-shirt? Vaseline and paper towels on a bedside table? Or was it all shameful and hidden, like boy scouts in a small prairie town? Guys slinking off into the paranoid refuge of some bottom deck storage area, slipping behind cartons of tinned peas & carrots to whip out their peckers while they riffled through Betty Grable playing cards?

That's the stuff I really wanted to know about. But try as I might I couldn't figure out how to politely phrase a question that'd get Lt. Phipps off the subject of torture training and into on-board sexuality. Perhaps Lt. Phipps realized my attention was wandering. At any

rate he carefully folded his cocktail napkin sketch into a tight wad and slipped it into his pants pocket.

'That's really something, eh?'

'I'll say!' I paused, clearing my throat, 'But Dave, tell me something – how much actual *space* does the crew have on board a nuclear submarine?' I watched while Lt. Phipps snapped open a fresh can of Coors. Would he catch my drift?

'We're talking about something a bit smaller than the inside of this seven-four-seven,' he replied laconically, 'that's *total* space, now, living *and* working.'

'Six weeks inside this little wee space? Seventy guys? *Wow.*'

'Oh, she's tight alright,' Lt. Phipps shot me a tense little smile, 'you get used to it, though. Like anything else – it's *there* so you learn to live with it. Mind you, it's a whole different ball game for a new recruit – green middies on their first cruise. Normally a greenie will have to hot bunk it – '

'Hot bunk it?'

'Yeah. There isn't enough sleeping space to go around so three greenies share the same bunk and sleep in rotation. Sixteen hours on duty, eight off to kip. Believe-you-me, *that* can get hairy for a young fella who's probably away from mom's cooking for the first time in his life.'

'No kidding!'

'But it's got its positive side, too. Hardship tends to pull the guys together. Greenies know that every peckerwood on board, right up to the skipper, has lived through the same kind of initiation – '

'Uh-huh.' I paused, sipped my beer. I wasn't so sure I knew how to politely volley that one. Probably better to change the mood, build up his confidence in me, maybe come back to the whacking-off issue from a different angle. I sipped my beer, waiting for Lt. Phipps to say something. He smiled too, clearly waiting for me to say something. I searched around.

'How about the nuclear reactor, Dave? Does that ever bother the guys?'

'*Bother* us?' Lt. Phipps blinked, befuddled.

'Well, yunno, you've got all that radiation underfoot for six weeks and – '

'Oh, *that* – Lordy, we're *totally* protected from that nonsense!' Lt. Phipps chuckled around a mouthful of cashews. 'Flow-through heavy water dampers inside a half-inch lead jacket. We never give the pile a second thought.'

'How about boredom, then – ?'

'Sure, you've got your boredom. Any routine job is boring. We tend to lean pretty heavily on our film programme,' Lt. Phipps stroked his moustache flat with two fingers, 'There's a two-hundred-film library on board that gets a top-to-bottom refit after every mission – everything from your Marx Brothers classic right down to the latest European stuff – you name a movie, fella, Phippsie's seen it! A hundred double features a year for twelve years,' Lt. Phipps looked straight into me, his grey eyes suddenly impish, 'multiply that one out and you're talking about a few thousand miles of film!'

I nodded eagerly, 'All-time favourites?'

'Not sure I believe in that *idea,*' Lt. Phipps said, suddenly serious. He reached up to pull the stewardess button so we'd get another beer. 'See, the way I look at it the whole film experience depends a lot on *intangibles.* You know, the kind of day I'm into, how our mission is shaping up, that kind of thing. But I *do* get off on Gene Kelly's work more than most, Kelly and Bobby DeNiro – you know, that hard-assed docu-drama trip he gets into – ?'

Bobby DeNiro? That hard-assed docu-drama trip? Mm-hm. I nodded absently and turned to look down into the night as the stewardess arrived to take the order from Lt. Phipps. Tried hard to visualize the restless Pacific 35,000 feet down – as if the air was transparent sea water. Tried to visualize closely-shaven men like Lt. Phipps ghosting under all that tons-per-square-inch pressure inside hand-tooled molybdenum tubes. Phipps playing darts a couple of feet away from the stockpile of Smart Torpedoes. The weaponry stacked end on end, a forest of gleaming hydrogen fists. Did they still scrawl cute nicknames on the warheads? *Little Man*? *Fat Boy*? Fancy up the business end with grinning jaws of shark's teeth? No doubt. The Doomsday scenarios locked inside pouches that required go-keys in sequenced combination, the keys worn around the necks of thick-eyed senior officers who'd probably spent thousands of hours sitting shoulder to shoulder in tiny screening rooms, Gene Kelly dancing while their titanium tube nosed along the floor of a pitch black ocean valley. Crossing and recrossing the International Dateline at thirty-five knots. A kind of suspended animation pods of grey whales would study from a cautious distance, squeaking up-dates to one another as they sonared the smooth, rapid shape. The whales shyly eavesdropping on the sub's fast-forward communications with those box-car-sized listening devices in the keyholes. Twenty million bucks worth of rare nickel alloys encrusted with neon blue barnacles big as your fist.

Sure, I thought, you can visualize that.

I returned my attention to Lt. Phipps as the ever-cheerful stewardess delivered four fresh cans of Coors, apparently pleased that at least a couple of hardy passengers were staying awake to break the monotony of her San Francisco to Guam leg. After Lt. Phipps had pulled the tab on a beer for me I lobbed him another softy, trying not to spook him while I felt around for a fresh approach to Jerk City.

'What about the air supply on board, Dave? How do you keep the air fresh when you're running submerged for six weeks?'

Lt. Phipps took a long suck on his beer and nodded his head vigorously, 'That's one of our *major* morale problems, my friend. Naturally, we got a state-of-the-art charcoal rinse that's s'posed to completely look after purification. It kind of scrunches up the soiled oxygen molecules and makes them sink to the bottom of this

ionized liquid,' Lt. Phipps showed me how, scrunching imaginary molecules between his hands. 'But – let's face it, eh? – no hardware *ever* delivers a top-end number. I mean, the smell isn't all *that* bad. We're talking *slight* residual odour. It's more a psychological thing. In the back of your mind you darn well *know* that once she pushes from Guam you're sealed in there with the recycled belches and farts from seventy sweaty guys for the next 42 days. Breathing the same old ass gas over and over again. You read me?' I had a crazy urge to cross my eyes and stick out my tongue but, sensing that I was heading for the other side of the world, I nodded politely instead. Lt. Phipps smiled, continued: 'Even with optimum diet the nutrition experts can't seem to get the incidence of flatulence down below five hits a day. Five times seventy fellas times forty-two days is a little over fourteen thousand bunnies – '

'That's a lot,' I said.

Lt. Phipps' face crinkled into a reassuring smile, 'I know it sounds crazy but you learn to live with it. It's a *slight* residual odour, right? I don't even notice it unless I'm *real* tired, maybe looking for something to bitch about at the end of a bad shift – it's not really that big a thing, a kind of cheesy aftertaste, know what I mean?'

'Of course I do,' I said, trying to imagine how Robertson Davies would handle the data I was receiving.

I looked out the window into the darkness again, sipped my beer and luxuriated in the depersonalized exhaustion which always accompanied a jet liner's sudden foreshortening of time. More than ever I had no clear sense why I'd decided to go where I seemed to be going. Until the previous day I'd been pacing up and down the shotgun hallway in my Montreal apartment, trying to decide whether or not it made sense to drop everything and head out to the airport. Hop a flight to the other side of the world. The point was, I'd just received the first news from Sarah in over 3 months. A postcard: the Taj Mahal lit by ghostly moon. According to the cramped printing Sarah was having an incredible time. *The* cosmic adventure! Chances were, the island of Bali would be her next stop-over. If she didn't decide to head for Katmandu instead. Or take the overland route to Rangoon. After turning the improbable adventure over and over in my mind I'd decided a trip to Indonesia was worth the financial and emotional risks. The risks get simpler when you know you're near the end of a love story, the pages thick in your left hand, thin in your right.

And now, perhaps it was Bali that waited beyond the curtained windows of the seaside bungalow where I lay, my phantom-mind trying to reconstuct conversations with a totally strange stranger. Desperately imagining some door out, or in, that would hinge on the daily routines aboard a nuclear submarine in 1982. The plain-spoken human reality behind 'a vigilant strategic posture for America's retaliatory capability.' All of it savagely true. Sinister, yet curiously fragile. Like settling back behind a handful of Percodan to watch Ronald Reagan host The Muppet Show. Suddenly, the mirror broke, released a bubble of pollen into the amber. Nothing left to smell except the place where I was.

Cheerless Resignation

I stood up and shuffled across the dim bedroom, rummaged in my rucksack until I located my bathing suit, stepped into it and wandered outside onto the patio. A sudden blast of thick scented tropical heat. Still stranger pollens. Hey, this was a neat hotel! That surf I'd been hearing was arriving on a magnificent white sand beach directly in front of my bungalow – it looked like a fucking travel brochure out there!

I ducked back inside the bungalow to pick up a package of cigarettes from the Duty Free Shop in Guam and the sandals D'arcy Hodges had given me on the eve of my departure.

Well-well-well, this was going to be *interesting*. I'd finally arrived on the other side of the world. Followed my nose until there was no direction to go in except 'back.' This was as foreign, as different, as it was ever going to get for me. I listened up into the warm air – that tropical warbler again – trotted down the patio steps and scanned the tree tops until I'd located the tangerine jab and flash of preening in the topknot of a nearby palm.

'This is Indonesia,' I reminded myself, 'you're in Bali now.'

This time the geographic reality clicked into place, overwhelming me with a sudden, wild exhilaration. Bali! That unspoiled paradise on the other side of the world! Hey! The story was finally *real*! *I* was real – the thread stretched out full-length behind me. *Anything* could happen now, and I was *ready*. My spirit remade in response to the furthest distance I'd ever travel. And maybe, incredible as it seemed, Sarah and I might even manage to talk it through one last time. Mystery. Mystery.

I lit a cigarettes, intoxicated with my apparent state of grace, and set off purposefully toward the beach. According to my watch it was 7:25.

Enormous combers, the biggest I'd ever seen, were coming in shore. The sea rising to stand in a steep wall as it caught bottom, the warm wind stripping feathers of spume as each wall peaked, held, and thunderclapped into itself, racing up the steep shoulder of talcum powder sand that sloped down from the fringe of towering palms. I chose a direction and started walking.

As I walked I imagined in my freshly-erased mind the various off-hand tactics I might employ when and if I met Sarah on the beach. What on earth would be in her eyes? Terror? Spacey disinterest? Joy, maybe? There was no way of knowing. At best, I might deserve what I got. At worst, I'd get what I deserved. Practically speaking, I hadn't even seen a detailed map of the island, had no idea whether a chance encounter was even possible during the dispensation of $300 in traveller's cheques.

Looking down the beach, staring at nothing, I suddenly realized I wasn't alone. A figure was emerging from the morning grey scale.

A running figure. A woman in a black leotard. Heading for me.

'A jogger?' I thought, 'I'm on the other side of the world and this is a jogger?'

Wondrously, yes. The woman in the black leotard was doing her morning set-up exercises. A hundred yards from me she stopped abruptly, faced the crashing surf and, hands on hips, began rotating her trunk in generous circles, lolling her head in counter-rhythm to unkink the muscles in her neck. I flipped my half-finished cigarette into the ocean and closed the distance between us at a leisurely pace. This woman in the black leotard was only the fourth person I'd encountered since I'd arrived in Bali – after the customs guy, the cab driver and the night clerk at the hotel – thus, the pending encounter promised special significance. Perhaps she was one of those free-spirited international vagabonds who, according to D'arcy hung out in places like Bali, Goa and Marrakesh, made them must-destinations for any retired coke dealer who was serious about 'doing the planet.'

By the time I got to her the young woman was doing deep knee bends, hands on hips as before. I knew she had to have noticed me in the corner of her eye but there was no acknowledgement of that as yet. Was there some unwritten protocol about these random encounters? I wasn't sure. The woman in the black leotard stopped doing her deep knee bends as I passed directly in front of her. I offered a little Cary Grant nod, doing my best, aloof and unconcerned, but she didn't in any way reciprocate it. In fact, she acted like I was a bad smell.

Probably a Kraut, I thought. I walked on for another couple of minutes and then stopped. There was at least a mile of beach ahead. Did I want to keep walking? Go right to the end of the beach? If not that, what? Head back toward my hotel and bump into Marlene Dietrich again? She'd think I was a new guy who didn't know his way around. No way I was gonna give her that satisfaction. Fuckin' Kraut. I turned and set off again, sooner or later I'd come to the something that signified the end. But what if I didn't? What if the beach went all the way around the island? Seventy-five miles of sand. Jesus, not even lunchtime and already the anxiety was closing in ... and what would I do if Sarah arrived from India with a friend, a young ... a young what? A young New Zealander, I decided. A handsome young New Zealander named Chet who'd been fortunate enough to share her refuge in a doorway during a chill winter downpour in Kabul. He'd be bluff, gruff and easy going – physically fit and intellectually unpretentious – a typical New Zealander off to see the world before he signed on with the family's chutney firm in Auckland. I knew it was crazy to be torturing myself like that on the other side of the world so I gave it up, began whistling tunelessly instead.

I must have walked for at least a mile. It was starting to get hot. Still no end in sight. Suddenly, a small cinnamon-coloured man in a sarong popped out of the palm trees ahead of me and headed down the slope of sand in a direct diagonal plotted to intersect my path. I continued to walk slowly, nodded hello as the little man – he couldn't have been more than five feet – greeted me with an incredible celebratory smile that showed gold bridgework and bright pink gums. Oddly, the little guy immediately fell into step alongside me. I should have felt like Peter O'Toole but I didn't. Too jumpy.

Finally, he said something: 'Where from?'

'I'm from Canada,' I replied, 'Been on the road for quite awhile. You know, kicking about – ' On the road for quite awhile? Kicking about? Had I actually said that to this innocent little Balinese man with the pink gums? Jesus, twenty hours ago I'd been washing socks in Montreal.

'Yes, yes, I know,' he replied quickly, accepting me at my word, 'It good here, yes? Lots girl. Lots sun. You like make the stone?'

I should have seen that one coming. The little chestnut man made a curious effort to connect with my gaze. The whites of his eyes were a cloudy yellow, like the troubled eyes one sees in the poorer districts of a North American city.

'I guess you're from around here,' I said, being bright.

The little cinammon-coloured man nodded vigorously and gave an abrupt laugh, almost a bark. 'Balinese number one. Sun. Girl. Big sea. Lots stone!' he smiled sheepishly, 'you got cigarette for me now?'

I lit another cigarette from the one I had going and handed it to him as we continued our walk, slower now because his stride was shorter than mine. We went on in silence like that for what seemed like a couple of minutes.

'Is Bali a big island?' Another brilliant lead from John Chancellor.

The little nut-brown man shook his head. 'Bali no big. Only States big. You come States, okay?'

'No, Canada,' I reminded him, 'Canada is just to the north of the United States. It's very big too. In fact, Canada's quite a bit bigger than the United States.'

The little man nodded, eager again, then smiled his gold teeth up to me. 'States number one for me too! Very big, States. You know Bee Gee?'

Oh brother. This guy had to be kidding. 'The Bee Gees?'

'Yeah, Bee Gee! Saturday Fever! Number one music for me! You know this Bee Gee?'

'Sure, I've heard of the Bee Gees,' I said. This wasn't fitting together all that well. Ahead of us the beach was narrowing, getting rocky. I tried to pick up my stride but the little man in the sarong restrained me, slowing down as if he knew something I didn't about what lay ahead. When I didn't slow down as much as he wanted me to the little Balinese grabbed my elbow and held me back.

'Something wrong?'

The little man shook his head. His cloudy eyes took on an intense and serious focus. 'You come States. I like States. You want make stone in Bali, right? I make best price for you.'

'I haven't any money,' I said, pointing to my bathing trunks. We smiled at each other. 'What are you selling?'

The little Balinese man pulled me close, 'I call Reggie. You money at hotel right now but you remember Reggie-face. Look you Reggie-face, okay?'

I nodded and looked into Reggie's face. We shook hands formally, as if meeting for the first time.

'I'll remember, Reggie.'

He pulled me closer still, his voice a husky whisper, 'Best *shmeck* all Bali. Bankok shit. All you want. Look you Reggie-face on this beach, okay?'

I smiled lamely and nodded as the little Balinese man named Reggie pumped my hand. A moment later he was trotting away up the shoulder of sand, waving back to me before he disappeared into the anonymous fringe of palm trees.

It took just under two hours to walk back along the beach to my hotel. The sun came fully into the sky, burning off the morning haze until even the furthest distances were crisply drawn.

As I walked I watched early arriving beach people, predominately young, athletic-looking Australian males, trail down from the palm trees and deploy their blankets and towels. Sunbathers had always made me nervous. At times their awesomely vacant rituals genuinely frightened me. Watching them settle on their little territories of sand I'd feel the entire visible world come to a menacing standstill, all possible choices of risk and fulfillment diminished to this one last, best choice, which was to wait on a skillet of sand while the roasting star climbed the sky overhead, the featureless day trailing behind like an empty banner.

When I passed close by the perimeter of their little groupings the young men lolled onto their elbows and eyed me briefly with solemn faces that neither asked nor offered anything. Then, slow as iguanas, they turned their attention elsewhere across the panorama of sea and sky, as if receiving some private communication on the solar wind. Here and there young women – deeply

tanned and beautiful like everyone else on the beach – came down in twos and threes to choose basking sites a little apart from the pods of males. Slipping demurely out of their bikini tops they massaged glistening oil into their bare breasts with almost medical seriousness, then lay down on their backs, faces hidden under floppy straw hats. No man-made sound interrupted the linear uniformity of this *tableau vivant* except, here and there, the tinkle and drone of toy-box melodies from a cassette deck – frail music that flitted above the rumble of surf and somehow fittingly completed the mood of cheerless resignation I attributed to each group of sunbathers I passed.

Picturing myself now, walking alone and vulnerable on that beach on the other side of the world, I realize that if anyone had said hello, smiled, or even welcomed me with a small gesture of the hand, I undoubtedly would have gratefully joined them on a corner of towel for the rest of the day. Pretended that that's what I'd wanted to do all along, filling their silences with half-truths and white lies about myself as the afternoon cooled toward amethyst sunset and our talk turned to dinner arrangements and the most soothing remedy for the sunburn on my chameleon shoulders.

As it was, I went back to my hotel and slept behind drawn drapes, the air conditioner a shunting engine in the switchyard of dreams.

The Universal Language

Late that afternoon I got out of bed and went for a walk. Ended up roaming around the village of Kuta, a grid of narrow dirt tracks secluded in a palm grove at my end of the beach. Before I'd gone a hundred feet down Kuta's main street I realized, again, what wide-bodied jumbos do to their 'destinations.' The village was a rat maze of ramshackle boutiques, bars and open kitchens, the streets packed shoulder to shoulder with deeply-tanned young Europeans and North Americans. I'd been at close quarters with this solemn tribe of New Age adventurers before. Their addiction to ritual self-adornment made me sick. The off-hand way they browsed past the make-shift stalls, the clamouring shopkeepers, trying to pretend they weren't actually searching for something to go with that *jelaba* from Morocco, those silk harem pants from Ibiza. I'm sure that I must have made them sick, too, sauntering around with that stupid superior grin on my face. The whole scene was so bloody embarrassing, so totally sleazy and corrupt, that it simply *had* to be somebody else's fault. I mean, we weren't a bunch of capitalist wimps seeing the world on daddy's credit cards. It wasn't us who dropped those orange peels and that Polaroid film wrapper in the middle of the fuckin' street. It wasn't *our* fault that the locals had started renting out surf boards, motorbikes and the bodies of their sisters. No way! Some other guy that left last month was responsible for all that ka-ka. All we wanted to do was pass through without leaving any footprints. Eat the local food. Don't spoil the people with big tips. Only staying a couple of days, actually – how much did you say you wanted for that monkey pelt?

I didn't say a word all that afternoon. Just wandered around and through the town and down to the beach and back to the rat maze of boutiques and around until I was on the beach again heading back to town, aimless yet purposeful, as if at any moment I might locate the long lost face of an old buddy in the anonymous crowd.

Only one thing I saw stuck with me. A group of Chinese children playing around a sand castle on the beach – they were deaf-mutes. I watched the way they communicated with hand signals, realized that I'd finally stumbled on a universal language. Nearby their mothers lounged in the shade of an enormous striped umbrella, laughing and heckling as they played Mah Jong. Tom Jones warbling on the cassette deck.

As soon as the sun set I started drinking Heineken.

Blonde on Blonde

Later the same evening – a bar, picnic tables open to the night air under a thatch roof. I'm sunburned and nearly drunk. I still haven't spoken to a soul, although I'm sharing my picnic table with a group of Australian men in their early thirties. So far I'm letting them think I'm a German. Some of the Aussies have just arrived, some have been here for months. They're having a reunion, slapping each other on the side of the head, the way Australian men do when they're excited. The Australians are telling each other how shitty Kuta is now, all these foreigners have spoiled it. You have to go way up into the mountains to see the *real* Bali. Rent a fuckin' motorbike! I can hardly understand their accents. I order more beer in German.

The world seems incredibly clear to me now. I am strangely cheerful. I sip beer in the fragrant night and watch young women pass in the street. Some of their faces hardly need to be changed at all. Others are light years off. Beautiful shapes polished by fire. I do my best. Any minute now I'm going to go out into the street and find someone who rents motorbikes. Get up early tomorrow morning and head for the mountains where the real people are. I've made up my mind but I order more beer to make sure. The Australians at my table are griping and groaning about the Melbourne girls from home who come to Bali and take native lovers, pay all the bills for the privilege of riding around on the back of a Honda, their arms wrapped hungrily around the slender waists of long-haired men wearing mirrored sunglasses. As far as the guys at my table are concerned these women are scum-sluts who deserve to get venereal worms and huge scalp scabs that make them go bald.

Tropical rain begins in the street a few feet from our table. I've been on the other side of the world for almost 24 hours and nothing fazes me. In fact, I'm nearly a Kraut. I order beer in German.

Order again. And again. I give a long-haired Balinese kid a fifty-dollar traveller's cheque as deposit for a motor bike rental. Maybe it was too much, I had no way of knowing. His eyes looked okay and I trusted him. I order more beer and they bring twice as much as I ordered. I take it anyway and give it to the Australians, nodding and saying *das es goot* when they try and thank me. The guy behind the bar is playing a badly popcorned copy of *Blonde on Blonde,* I put my head down on the picnic table and doze, listening while the Australians shout out the words they remember.

Then, the music is gone. It's not raining anymore. The bar is deserted. The proprietor is stacking chairs on the tables. I get up to leave and he comes over and asks me for a tip. I give him an American single and he takes it and turns away without looking at me. The streets are wet and empty. It takes me over an hour to find my hotel. I decide to sleep fully clothed in a chair on the porch, the noisy war of insects all around me. Dozing off, I hear myself repeat: 'Forget it, forget it, forget it.'

Hypnotic Curves

The long-haired Balinese kid who'd taken my fifty-dollar traveller's cheque didn't show up next morning and, when I reported this at noon to the desk clerk, he told me I should be more careful, there were some shady operators in Kuta. Since it was Saturday there weren't any policemen on duty – did I want to try and file a complaint anyway? I said not to bother and cashed another two fifty-dollar traveller's cheques, strolled into town and, within ten minutes, found a guy who rented me his Honda for seven bucks, even showed me how to get on the road to Sacred Mount Agung, the day trip I'd heard the Australians talking about.

Then, just like that, I was somewhere else. Kuta disappearing behind me as the road wound its way up into terraced foothills, the tropical wind whipping and snapping my shirt out behind me. Hey, this was more like it!

As the pitch steepened the Honda's engine laboured and I slowed down. Slowed down even more for the little clusters of palm trees that sheltered the family compounds of each village. Coasting through the villages I waved to tiny kids who scampered to the roadside, squealing: 'hi!hi!hi!hi!', bouncing up and down with giggles as I down-shifted, released the throttle with my right hand and returned their manic waves, shouting: 'Hi-i-i!' Coasting by them toward thicker clusters of townsfolk, little men in colourful sarongs talking by the side of the road, their faces filled with gaiety, as if I'd provided them with the best punchline of the day.

In the course of my two-hour ride to the sacred mountain I passed two cremation festivals – the public ground that connected each cluster of family compounds jammed with busy, happy people – the men clambering around multi-levelled cremation towers of bamboo and coloured paper, the women and children down below preparing elaborate banquets for visitors from neighbouring villages who would soon arrive. In the centre of all this blazingly colourful activity, a fifteen-piece gamelan band tuned the still afternoon air with a polyphonic maze of counter-rhythms that chased each other endlessly around the curves of a hypnotic melody. At one of the villages I dismounted and hunkered inconspicuously by the side of the road, smoking cigarettes while I watched the funeral preparations. The villagers went about their business with scarcely a nod in my direction. When, as periodically happened, I caught the attention of one of the men working on the scaffold around the cremation bier, he perhaps pausing to roll his own cigarette, we simply returned raised eyebrows, a characteristic acknowledgement among the Balinese signifying something like: 'Not bad, eh?'

Sacred Monkeys

At four o'clock I reached the top of the road, the foot of Sacred Mount Agung. It was drizzling and I could see three rainbows at

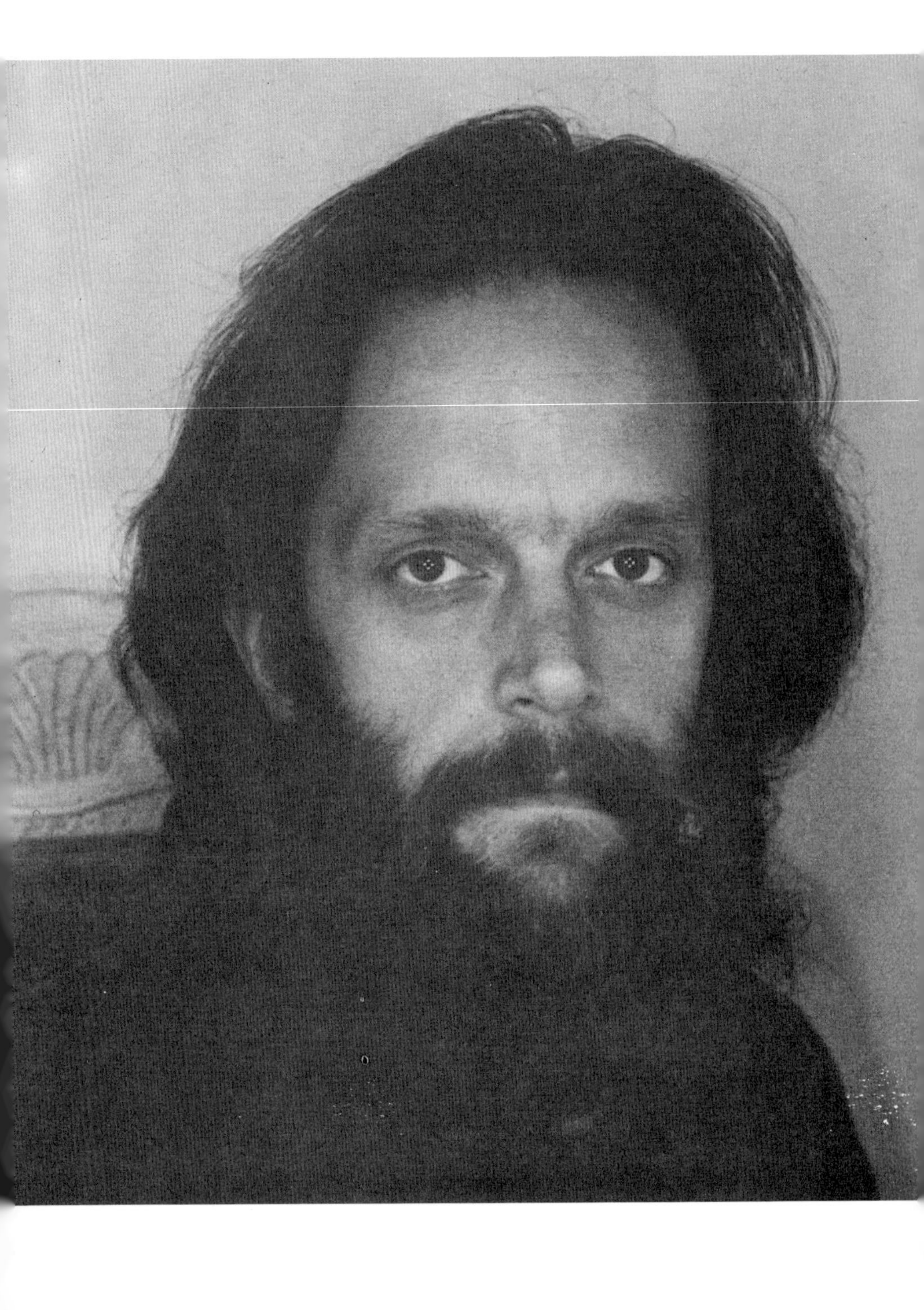

once against the nubbly green corduroy of the volcano. For an hour or so I squatted in the drizzle and watched the landscape change, interrupted only once when a busload of Japanese tourists stopped long enough for snapshots. I helped some of them, operating their sophisticated cameras so they could be in their own pictures, the dark badge of my shadow falling diagonally across their feet. I think it was there at the foot of Sacred Mount Agung that my mind's reservoir reached the overload threshold beyond which it won't assimilate new stimulii. As often happens in those instances, the story went on without me.

Perhaps I coasted the motorbike down through those surrounding hills with the engine switched off, let gravity whisper me past elderly women using tasselled bamboo wands to drive flocks of geese back from another day of fattening in the complicated staircase of a flooded rice terrace. Perhaps I tried to memorize the way the sculpted waterworks accentuated the intuition of the sky, perhaps watched the sails of cloud fall into one of those steep, manicured valleys, reflections fractured in a broken mirror. Perhaps I thought about Sarah and how I would meet her if the story came true and allowed me to enter it.

As it was, sometime later I found myself following road signs to the famous Ullu Watta cliff temple on the south coast of the island. Flying now, roaring across dry, brittle flatland – scrub-dotted vistas of red laterite punctuated by gnarled cacti and thin white cattle. The sun was nearly gone. It drizzled on and off. Strangely, I was at peace with myself. I knew I would cash my last traveller's cheque and go back to the other side of the world. I knew that I'd probably never see Sarah again.

The sun was six inches off the horizon when I reached the Ullu Watta Temple. It started to rain hard again, a denser version of the light tropical drizzle that misted the island every couple of hours.

A half-dozen children trotted toward me from a thatched refreshment stand as I leaned my motorbike on its kickstand. They

clustered close and began trying to sell me things – fine silver chains, jade rings, wood carvings, batik sarongs. I pushed past them, shaking my head, and made for the stone staircase that obviously led up to the ruin. A man at the bottom of the staircase motioned for me to take off my sandals so I did. He held out a little wooden tray for an offering and I gave him some paper money. He pointed up the staircase, said: 'You feed sacred monkey?'

I shrugged and he retrieved a little cellophane bag of peanuts from inside his loose shirt and handed them to me. I exchanged money for the peanuts and headed up the massive stone stairs, smiled hello to a badly sunburned family of British people on their way down. The drizzle thickened as I stepped past the stone dragons that guarded the portal to the temple. The sacred space was a roofless stone rectangle contained inside a waist-high parapet – a platform cantilevered over the edge of a cliff, the blue-black Pacific heaving against the shore thirty-five stories below.

A small shrine thickly ornamented with stone deities occupied a raised platform in the centre of the space. For a moment it rained hard. I took shelter under the lip of its thatched roof as the downpour peaked and atomized back to drizzle. I lit a cigarette and watched the match burn towards my fingers, then dropped it to fizzle on the damp pavement. The nearest stone god glowered at me, his face a ferocious bulge of eyes, cheeks and mouth. I tried to look past the surface and into the stone, like E.M. Forster, but it didn't work. This wasn't English 101. I was waiting for the rain to stop under the sheltering thatch of a Hindu shrine on the other side of the world. I was walking to the parapet to look straight down at the ocean, then along the sheer wall of cliff that stretched away in both directions. I was, on realizing that I had a small bag of peanuts in my hand, looking up to search the broad-leafed boughs of an overhanging tree. There were no sacred monkeys in sight so I put the bag of peanuts into an alcove between two gods. There was already another bag of unopened peanuts there, plus a Kodak film

wrapper. I decided that I'd probably seen what there was to see at the Ulla Watta Temple and headed back down the stairs. The sun was setting.

My sandals weren't where I'd left them at the bottom of the staircase and the man who'd taken my offering and sold me the sacred peanuts was nowhere in sight. As I stood there trying to figure out what to do the gaggle of kids I'd dealt with in the parking lot left the shelter of the refreshment stand and trotted up to meet me with their flight bags full of local handicrafts.

I waved them away, said: 'I won't even look at that shit until I get my sandals back. I left my sandals right here and now they're gone. Do you understand – *sandals*?' I pointed to my bare feet.

The eldest of the boys, a full head taller than his companions, pushed his way toward me with a big grin. He pointed down the hill to the pop stand, 'You shoe *dry* – my grandmother! Come!' He pushed the other boys away as they started proffering their silver chains and wood carvings, said something sharp to make them follow in silence as he led me down the hill toward the pop stand. The little wrinkled lady behind the waist-high chest cooler that occupied the space under the thatch handed my sandals across and grinned showing empty gums, then put a large tumbler of pink juice down in front of me. I finished the glass in one swallow and put it down in front of her with a smile.

'Grandson! Grandson!' she said eagerly, pointing behind me to the group of boys who stood waiting a few feet away, wide-eyed and ready for a bargaining session. The eldest, the one who had silenced the others and led me to my sandals, nodded and pointed to the old woman behind the cooler: 'Grandmother!' he said. 'What you name?'

I told him my name and he repeated it to the others who in turn repeated it to each other, giggling. 'I Johnny,' the kid said.

'Glad to meet you, Johnny,' I offered my right hand and all the boys jostled each other as Johnny pumped it, his eyebrows arched

BANCES
IMPORTED

in wonder, as if I was about to produce a flapping cockatoo from the space between our palms.

I finished a second glass of juice and put it back on the stainless steel lid of the cooler.

Johnny said: 'You buy with me now?'

'I don't think so, Johnny. But why don't you show me what you have,' I pointed to my eye, 'show me what you have,' and Johnny nodded eagerly and pointed into the hands of the little boys who surrounded us.

'Like batik? Like carving from Ramayana? This Prince Rama – '

'How about jewellery?' I asked, 'My girlfriend likes jade. You have jade?'

'Jade? Oh yes, I show you special jade – ' the boy said something to the old woman behind the counter and she hustled back into the shadows of the hut, returned a moment later to place a cloth wrapped bundle on top of the cooler, unwrapping it reverently as the young boy moved close to me to begin his sales pitch.

'You know story this jade?'

I said I didn't and he reached into the package the old woman offered and withdrew a smooth lump of polished jade about the size of an ostrich egg. He held out the piece of jade and pointed to a blotchy red stain on one of its faces.

'This jade from Bali funeral, very special, very old, very vieux – you French man, okay?'

I told him I was from Canada and let him put the lump of jade in my hand. 'This isn't jewellery, Johnny. No jade jewellery?'

The boy shook his head seriously and tapped the red stain on the piece of jade I held in my hand. 'You no understand. This jade come Bali funeral – '

When I didn't register that he retrieved the jade from my grasp, clutched it to his breast and looked skyward like an El Greco martyr. 'We make like this! Put like this! Come fire! Flames! Very *big*!' he waved his arms around to indicate that he meant the place where we stood would be completely engulfed, 'after fire come this,' he pointed to the red stain, 'this red come soul,' he tapped it, 'soul. You understand?'

'From the soul,' I said, 'yes, I think I understand – '

'Yes! Yes! Bali funeral, big fire! Then – ' he tapped the red stain. It looked like an iron deposit.

'Beautiful, but – '

'Good! Very good!' The little lady behind the counter rasped as I hefted the jade from hand to hand, 'This come *grandfather.* You buy?'

I tried to hand the jade back to the kid named Johnny but he wouldn't take it.

'You Canada,' he said, 'I know Canada. I make special price for Canada!'

'How much?' I said, still trying to put the lump of jade back into his hands.

'Six thousand,' he said seriously, 'I give you twelve fronk – '

I shook my head. 'I haven't got that much money, Johnny. Thanks anyway, but – '

'You give States dollar? I make this jade *ten* States dollar! Five thousand rupee, okay?'

Since he'd already come down two bucks on the exchange I decided to test the boundary. Just for the heck of it. 'Five. I'll give you five U.S.'

'No *five*!' He tapped the red stain excitedly, 'look you all Bali you no find funeral jade for *five.* This *soul*! *Tres vieux*! I say I make you ten,' he paused and, when I didn't in any way respond, got very serious, came close to me as if to share a secret, 'Make me *last* price.'

What on earth was I doing? I hefted the lump of jade from hand to hand like a baseball.

'I'll give you six bucks,' I said, 'that's my last price.'

Johnny said something to his grandmother and she said something back to him.

'You like beer?' he asked, 'she give you beer. You no pay.'

'Okay.' I put the lump of funeral jade on the cooler top and lit a cigarette as Johnny's grandmother opened me a beer and poured it into my juice glass. It was going to be dark soon. I finished the beer in two swallows and let them know that I was ready to leave.

Johnny picked up the lump of jade and forced it back into my hands. 'Bali people no sell this jade – make me last price.'

'I told you, Johnny,' I said, shuffling out of the hut, trying unsuccessfully to transfer the jade back into his hands, 'I haven't got much money. This is very beautiful but my girlfriend wants jewellery, she couldn't – '

'Make me best price!' Something close to anger was moving into the kid's eyes, 'I say you this come *soul*! *Tres vieux*! No sell this in Bali! Make me *last* price!'

Johnny was blocking my path. 'I told you I won't go any higher than six bucks. Six U.S.'

Johnny and his grandmother exchanged quick whispers. She shook her head violently and tried to snatch the funeral jade out of my hands but the kid restrained her with a sharp rebuke. She shook her head more violently, squealed: *'DEECE!'* but the kid silenced her again, smiled solemnly toward me.

'You hard bargain, Canada. I make you this jade six dollar if you buy one more jade from this woman. She *poor*. She *old*. She no want to sell this jade. Look you all Bali, you no find this jade!'

It was raining again. 'Listen, Johnny, I told you, I don't really want this. If you insist I'll give you six bucks for it, okay? Listen, it's starting to rain and I really have to – '

'Six buck okay for me,' the kid said as I began to walk away, 'My grandmother give you for six. You keep *special* all you life. You give me six U.S. now?'

I gave the kid named Johnny six bucks. In ten minutes it'd be pouring again and I wanted to be on the road before that happened. Johnny followed me over to my motorbike, carrying his

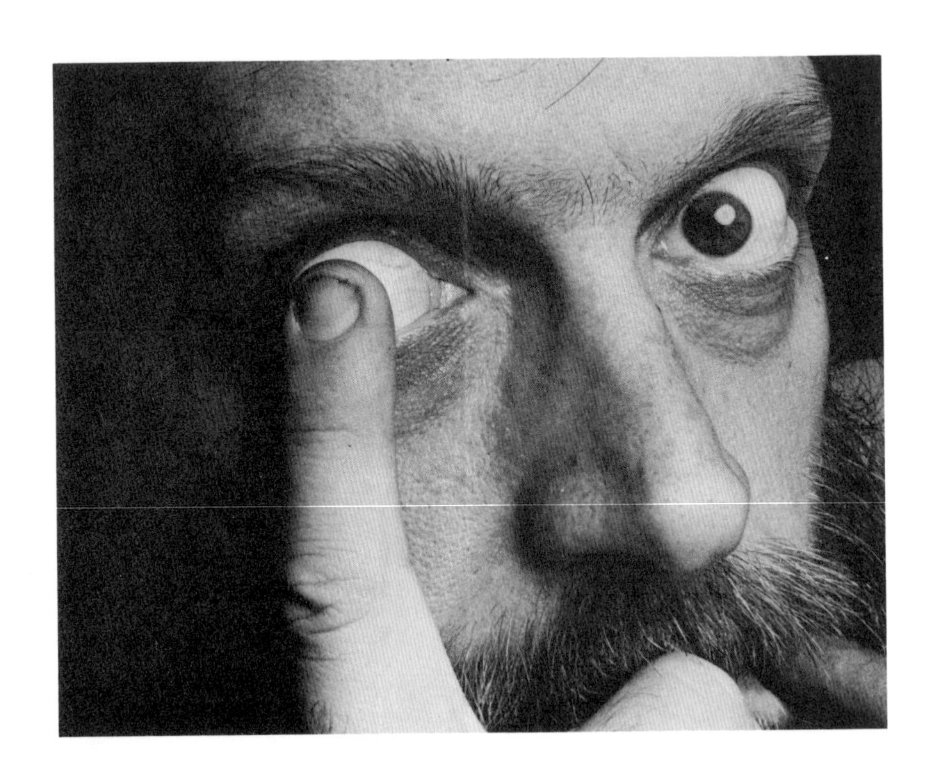

grandmother's parcel of funeral jade. He watched as I tipped the bike off its kickstand and threw my weight onto the starter pedal, straddled the front tire and held it between his knees as the engine caught.

'You States,' he said, glancing nervously toward the empty doorway of the pop stand, 'I like States. My grandmother very sick. She love this jade but she old. *Tres pauvre.* Now I give you special jade from my sister. She dead *two month*! Look you!'

Before I could make a move the kid had retrieved another lump of funeral jade from his grandmother's pouch. When I refused to take it he balanced the turquoise boulder precariously on my gas tank and pointed to a red stain. 'From sister. See? Still *wet*! Two month! *Fresh*! I give you this one thousand rupiah. Two States dollar. Okay?'

Wait a second, I thought, I'm confused. This is a bigger lump of funeral jade with a brighter red stain on it and this kid is trying to sell it for a fraction of what I paid for the other one.

'Johnny, I paid five thousand for a *little* piece. Now you say a thousand for this big one, why?'

Johnny pretended he didn't understand what I was talking about. 'You States. I like States. I say you one thousand. This soul come older sister! Two month! What you best price! Make me *last* price.'

Johnny had me going and he knew it. 'I'll give you five hundred.' I said, 'Five hundred is the last price.'

Johnny smiled thinly and took my money, helped me fit the larger lump of funeral jade into my shoulder bag. I kicked the bike into gear and let out the clutch but he blocked my path, held up the sagging cloth pouch containing the rest of his grandmother's funeral jade, tried to force it into my hands.

'You hard bargain, Canada,' he said as I tentatively tried to walk the motorbike around him, 'I give you all this jade for two States dollar, okay? Make me *best* price!'

I coasted past Johnny and his bag of souls, pretended he'd suddenly turned invisible as I gunned the motorbike up the dirt track that led back to the main road.

'Two hundred!' he called after me. '*Doo Fronk!*'

At the top of the track I stopped and turned around to watch Johnny scamper back toward the old woman who tottered out of the pop stand to meet him, the other children crowded close, jostling and giggling, as the old woman pointed up the ridge toward me and shrieked with laughter.

Suddenly the frame pulled back and I saw myself from a great distance – a tiny figure on a motorbike heading across an empty plateau. From that moment onward I knew I was heading home.

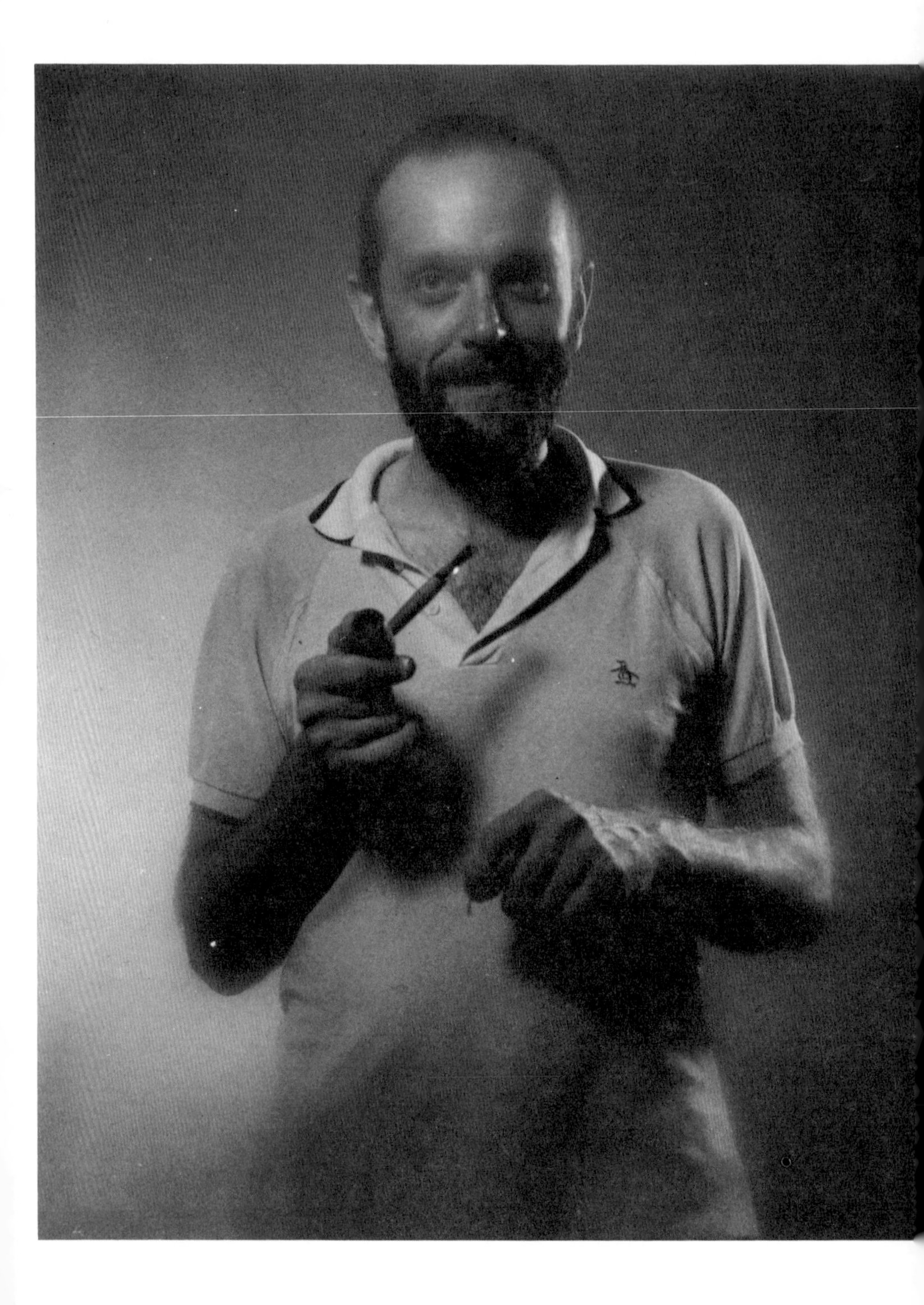

Palimpsest

The Minutes of the Last Meeting

Sailor take warning. We've entered the latitudes of a mind yet more distant. Now it really is five years later. Nothing left between us and that sunny July afternoon on Georgian Bay except these minutes. When we've read them through to the end this chapter of the Flat Earth Society will disband for good.

A Self-erasing Tape

This isn't a story about wild irises or the ancient rock of Georgian Bay. It's not one of those sprawling yarns you could drive a truck through. It has nothing to do with sitting in the middle of the Atlantic Ocean. Nor those who loiter mid-Pacific waiting to lob a hot one on the Kremlin. No good guys and bad guys here. No white hat named Phipps. No black dog answering to Shaddrach. We won't be taking any more long walks under street lamps with the families of shadows opening and closing around us like petals. That journey is over. *We're through answering questions with questions.*

Here is the recognition: no story can set the world on fire, or save it from the flames. *No language can describe how it will feel when we wake up in pitch black and hear the hounds baying, the cocks crowing. We're children in a schoolyard trying to perfect the practices of mind travel. The world as it was is the same as the world as it is. Only the mystery changes.*

Angels in the Snow

She knew where I was going when I woke up in the dark this morning and slipped away from her bed. She could have said something. Instead she pretended she was asleep. A couple of hours later I heard her moving back and forth between the bedroom and the bathroom. She was humming. When she was ready to leave for work she padded in here, wordlessly took me by the wrist and towed me into the next room. She laid me down on the couch and cradled my head in her lap, stroked it like I was a cat. She knew what I was thinking about but she wasn't going to give in to it. After a minute or two of silent staring I asked her what she was looking at. She blinked, smiled, said I looked like one of those life-size dolls that can say *maah,* maybe move its arms a bit. That was about it. I laughed for a moment but she didn't join me. Another silence. In a quiet voice Sarah asked me if I had any idea where it was going. Before I could think up an answer she told me to quit worrying. If it sounded like a bunch of hayseeds singing God Bless America around a Thanksgiving turkey that was okay with her too.

'Who remembers the last two minutes of a movie?'

I nodded and stared into her more deeply. 'What are you saying?'

She smiled down at me, whispered: 'Get that little fucker out of this apartment, okay?' That one earned her a hard pinch – she yelped to her feet and scampered giggling from the room.

From the hall: 'Which coat d'you want?'

'Oh darling, which coat do *you* want?' A moment later she was back in the room zipping up my down jacket.

'And another thing – quit answering questions with questions. Forget the theories, okay?'

'Yessum, Missy Stalin.' I was following her across the room to the front door. She pulled it half open and turned to face me, held up her gloved hand and made it into a little puppet with a thumb for a jaw.

'Hi! I'm Walter Mitty,' her gloved hand squeaked, 'I'm your secret friend!' That got a good laugh. I pulled the door fully open for her, gave a little wave. 'See you later, Walt – '

The puppet turned a quick double-take to Sarah, squealed: 'But Mister Writer – *wait!* Walter Mitty's got some *advice* for you!'

I had the door half closed. 'Make it snappy, Walt.'

Walter Mitty flicked a glance at Sarah, cleared his throat. 'Keep it simple ... dickhead.' That did it. I threw the door open and lunged at her, pinned her against the opposite wall in the stairwell. After I landed a couple of pretty good rabbit punches Sarah started to giggle, began laughing out of control when I got her in a bear hug and made like I was planning to drive my knee straight up into her crotch. She retaliated with a playful knee of her own – a little too close for comfort – then managed to free one of her arms, turned her gloved hand back into Walter Mitty and pushed him into my face.

'Hey! Never too late to start some therapy!' Mitty shrilled, 'How 'bout a little hot tub and some rapping?' I clamped my hand over Sarah's mouth and pinned her tight to the wall. For a moment we laughed and struggled against each other, then we stopped, loosened our grips. Sarah closed her eyes slowly and kissed me on the mouth.

'Don't worry.'

'Who's worried?'

Her eyes popped open. 'And don't lie! You're *not* a coward.'

'I know,' I lied.

She paused, staring at me like my skin was changing colour.

I sighed: 'Just tell me how to think about it.'

'Just because *it's* over doesn't mean *you're* over, dummy! It's too late for all that Mount Rushmore crap!

'But I don't – '

'Yes you *do*! You said it all last night!'

'I did?'

'C'mon now,' Sarah put her hands on my shoulders and gave me a little shake, 'You promised me that you'd point toward the simplest thing that's true in your heart, talk about it for a couple of minutes, then say your bye-byes. Right?'

I shrugged. 'Sure, whatever – listen, see you later, okay?'

A final flash of smile and she was clumping down the stairs and I was back inside, the door latch about to click shut when she threw that little hand puppet voice again. I stuck my head around the corner and looked down the stairs, Sarah was holding Walter Mitty up toward me.

'Not even gonna say goodbye to your secret pal?' he pouted.

'G'bye Walter.'

I waved. Mitty shot Sarah a dubious look, then turned back to me.

'Hey, Mister Writer! *I* believe in you!'

'I believe in you too, Walt,' I said.

Sarah lowered her arm slowly, put the gloved hand behind her back, stared at me like it was the first time.

'Something real, okay?'

'Something real,' I said.

'Tomorrow's a new day.'

'I won't forget.'

'Promise?'

I nodded. She nodded back, then I watched her wheel her bike out onto the front porch. A moment later I was back in the apartment, leaning against the door while I stared at the ceiling. I let out a long breath and closed my eyes. Realized that I was finally hearing it in my head. A voice was repeating the words of the last sentence over and over again, arranging and rearranging the words until the sentence was as simple as the thing it wanted to say. For a moment it shone, then its shining was an echo, then the echo of an echo chambered by a grand silence. The heart, tomorrow.

David Young
was born in Oakville, Ontario in July 1946.
He currently lives and works in Toronto.

Jim Lang
was born in August 1941 in Cleveland, Ohio,
where he is presently involved in forensic and
medical photography.

Typeset in Baskerville and printed in Canada.

For a list of other books you might enjoy,
write for our catalogue of books in print,
or call us at (416) 979-2217.

THE COACH HOUSE PRESS
401 (rear) Huron Street,
Toronto, Canada M5S 2G5